The IEA Health and Welfare Unit

Choice in Welfare No 50

160 718950 X

D0308973

# The Realities of Rationing: 'Priority Setting' in the NHS

## John Spiers

**with practitioners' experiences of rationing**

## Harry Burns
## Bob Gilbertson
## Karol Sikora

IS 239/02??

IEA Health and Welfare Unit
London

First published April 1999

The IEA Health and Welfare Unit
2 Lord North St
London SW1P 3LB

© The IEA Health and Welfare Unit 1999

*All rights reserved*

ISBN 0-255 36453-9
ISSN 1362-9565

CARDIFF UNIVERSITY
12 JUL 1999
PRIFYSGOL CAERDYDD

Typeset by the IEA Health and Welfare Unit
in New Century Schoolbook 10.5 point
Printed in Great Britain by
The Cromwell Press
Trowbridge, Wiltshire

# Contents

# The Authors

**John Spiers** is an External Professor in the Business School at the University of Glamorgan. He is a Senior Research Fellow and member of the Advisory Council of the IEA Health and Welfare Unit. He is a Visiting Fellow of the NHS Staff College, Wales, and of the King's Fund Management College and has been Health Policy Adviser at the Social Market Foundation since 1994. He served on a series of NHS Executive and Ministerial advisory committees in the Department of Health between 1991 and 1998, and was a member of the Prime Minister's Advisory Panel on the Citizens' Charter. He is a former chairman of the Patients' Association, of Brighton Health Authority and of Brighton Health Care NHS Trust. In 1986 the book publishing firm of which he was founder and chairman won the Queen's Award for Export Achievement. He is a well known broadcaster and has lectured widely on health care in the UK, and in Europe, America, Asia, and Australia. In 1993 he established the first ever Clinical Performance Improvement Unit in the NHS.

His writings include *The Invisible Hospital and the Secret Garden: An Insider's Commentary on the NHS Reforms*, Oxford: Radcliffe Medical Press, 1995; *Who Owns Our Bodies? Making Moral Choices in Health Care*, Oxford: Radcliffe Medical Press, 1997, and *Dilemmas in Modern Health Care* (editor), Social Market Foundation/Profile Books, 1997.

**Harry Burns** graduated in medicine from the University of Glasgow in 1974. Over the next 15 years he worked as a general surgeon and for the last six years of his surgical career was a consultant surgeon at the Royal Infirmary in Glasgow. He entered health care management and was, for a time, Medical Director of the Royal Infirmary in Glasgow. Since 1993 he has been Director of Public Health for Greater Glasgow Health Board which is responsible for organising health care and maintaining the health of one million people in the West of Scotland. In 1999 he was awarded a Visiting Professorship in Public Health Medicine, University of Glasgow.

**Bob Gilbertson** is one of six partners at the Highcliffe Medical Centre, Christchurch, Dorset. The practice is third wave fund-holding and first wave Personal Medical Services PCAP Pilot. It cares for probably the oldest patient demography in the country (44 per cent over 65 years).

Since becoming senior partner in 1992 and abolishing the post, he has implemented an extensive programme of team building and re-engineering which now includes everyone who is employed by or attached to the Medical Centre. A flourishing Patient Participation Group is regarded as one of the teams and is closely involved in the strategic planning of the practice. For this work he was awarded the Searle/Royal College of General Practitioners (Wessex Faculty) 1999 GP Award. He is married with four adult children.

**Karol Sikora** is chief of the World Health Organisation's cancer programme. Based at the International Agency for Cancer Research in Lyon, his mission is to reduce the global incidence, mortality and suffering caused by cancer. He is on secondment from his post as Professor of Clinical Oncology at Imperial College School of Medicine, Hammersmith Hospital, London. He studied medicine at Cambridge and the Middlesex Hospital and, after registrar posts at St Bartholomew's Hospital, became a research student at the MRC Laboratory for Molecular Biology in Cambridge. After obtaining his PhD he spent a year as a clinical fellow at Stanford University, California, before returning to direct the Ludwig Institute in Cambridge. He has been Clinical Director for Cancer Services at Hammersmith for 12 years. He established a major cancer research laboratory funded by the Imperial Cancer Research Fund. He is a member of the UK Health Department's Expert Advisory Group on Cancer and the Committee on Safety of Medicines.

# *Foreword*

This book examines the realities of rationing in the NHS. Professor John Spiers contributes a substantial essay dealing with the cultural, political, and economic challenges of rationing. He is followed by three contributions from distinguished medical practitioners who spend their lives at the 'sharp end' of care.

Professor Karol Sikora is one of the world's leading experts on cancer. Dr Harry Burns is a former hospital clinician who is now a leading purchaser of health services in one of our largest urban areas. And Dr Bob Gilbertson is a GP working in an area noted for a significant concentration of elderly people.

They each reflect the stresses and compromises of a rationed service. The three doctors offer a number of messages to consider. These include the ideas that rationing is unnecessary, because health spending could be significantly higher; that rationing is necessary at any level of expenditure, but its principles should be explicit; and, that rationing as it now functions obliges clinicians to make difficult and sensitive choices, denying services to some in order to supply others.

Dr Bob Gilbertson makes it clear that there is a great deal of adaptation and improvisation in making things work as well as possible in general practice. This can include much more patient 'involvement' in decision-making. The role of Patient Partnership Groups offers intriguing possibilities which need full consideration. Are they to have power to set protocols? Are they to be purely advisory, like focus groups? Is this a shift of leadership, away from an exclusive role for doctors? How is this to be institutionalised? How and by whom would new leaders be designated and empowered?

Rationing, clearly, is a daily fact of life in the NHS. Is it really unavoidable? Dr Harry Burns argues that he is not against rationing if a service genuinely cannot be afforded. Yet he suggests that this proposition has not been properly tested. He suggests that we should not ration services before there has been a proper public debate about how health care can be funded adequately. He takes issue with the argument that rationing (and a national 'core' service) is inevitable to discipline unlimited demand. Moreover, in his view, the NHS does not seek to address unlimited demand, but 'need'. Dr Burns believes that there is no evidence of unlimited need, and that the basis of rationing is thus economic.

Within a system of state-rationed 'needs' patients and professionals find they are, necessarily, in a beggar-my-neighbour situation. For, in a system of limited funding, if one patient does better, another must be the loser. Professor Karol Sikora discusses this problem as it arises for cancer patients. He, like many professionals, is clearly uncomfortable about making rationing decisions which conflict with professional ethical principles which put the patient first. Health planners talk of 'populations', but clinicians meet people. Dr Burns suggests why and how it is difficult to apply explicit rationing schemes in practice. Professor Sikora argues for a more explicit rationing process.

Professor Sikora argues that value judgements have to be made and reconciled in the eternal decision-making triangle of patient, doctor and payer. These are judgements case by case, and often between individuals competing for similar (and insufficient) resources. Which patients are the more deserving, who is to decide, how, and on what basis? These choices come up every day in decisions concerning capacity to benefit from treatment.

Under the NHS, the deficits between the promise and the provision are often very significant. The essays in this book explore current realities and suggest that there is a large potential for enhanced capacity in the UK. They prompt questions about alternative ways to finance improved service quality, which would give people access to appropriate services when and where they want them.

*David G. Green*

# The Realities of Health Care Rationing in the NHS

## John Spiers

# 1

# Rationing: The Challenge of PPE

Nature rations us all.

We are all different, all born unequal, all with different parentage, inheritance, DNA, intelligence, mental capacities and physical characteristics. Most of us are accustomed to living with ourselves, and to doing our best to explore and extend our possibilities. However, in health care we often have surprisingly little autonomy and self-responsibility.

Few really believe that health care can be 'free', or that we can have it all. Most of us assume that in health care, as in daily life, cost conscious choices have to be made, trade-offs negotiated, options given up. There is a price to be paid for everything. We know that we cannot get everything we want, when we want it, how we want it, and at no cost. We know intuitively that rationing is inevitable, and that there must be cost-conscious choices. However, in health care this is made unnecessarily difficult—and indeed much worse than it need be—by the public-sector monopoly of the NHS. We are not enabled to ration for ourselves as in so much of our 'other' life. An insistence on the paramountcy of *political* objectives—re-distribution, equality, 'justice'—damages health objectives. The refusal, albeit with benign intentions and honest convictions, to support creative, dynamic, innovative, competitive provision denies benefits to many patients. Crucially, the benefits of investment, productivity and choice evident in the wider modern economy, and obtainable only through competitive enterprise, are lost within the NHS.

These are the key points as we ask what causes the present difficulties with rationing and how they might be remedied. The question is, why is there a gap between supply and demand and what can be done about it, as an alternative to state rationing in a public-sector monopoly? Can change be achieved which will enable both better health care and social solidarity to be secured, but without the coercive disadvantages of a public-sector monopoly? This essay identifies the deficits and denials of the NHS, and explores this question. It offers some practical proposals, drawing on examples in place in other countries. It offers a contrast between what exists in the NHS with what might instead be available to all patients, while at the same time reducing health inequalities.

There is a pervasive dislike of placing the blame for insufficient funding, capacity and service where it belongs. This resistance often expresses itself in moral terms. It conceals the fact that subsidy, rationing, and the removal of prices are the fundamental recipe for scarcity. Rationing is a concise and an inevitable consequence of making policy by financial targets. The alternative is to improve productivity by emphasising the necessity of competitiveness and service quality. This advance can only occur in response to costed demand. One-time cost savings—by eliminating waste and inefficiency—combined with more 'justice' in rationing, will not suffice. They are tinkering in the margins.

There are social and economic questions to be answered. How can we get more cost-effective services, greater choice, success in preventing diseases, treatments which work and a guarantee of care for all? How can we get dramatic and sustained cost reductions, increases in productivity and individual responsibility? How can we reconcile economic and social goals?

To make progress we need to abandon illusion. I argue in this essay that we are all unequal and that life is not 'fair'; that a public-sector monopoly in health care makes this worse, not better; that this is a problem for government and for the individual; that self-responsible moral behaviour depends on significant changes in the culture, funding and purchasing of health care. The key philosophical point on self-responsibility was succinctly stated by Enoch Powell: 'there is no meaning in responsibility where there is no power... we cannot be responsible for doing what we cannot do'.[1]

This essay urges that differences between people matter, and should not be submerged or eliminated. It is the market which uniquely makes differences between people matter. It singularly empowers them to the benefit of all. Powell, again, makes a key point here about coherence in society:

> the true mutual respect between human beings rests upon the recognition, without any implication of superiority or inferiority, of differences —differences between one individual and another, differences between one society and another.[2]

Monolithic, public-sector monopoly suppresses the responsiveness necessary for each individual to be fulfilled in obtaining health services which specifically concern personal, intimate, separable and timely benefits. Necessarily, too, monopoly increases costs, which are lowered by competitive supply. For costs can only be controlled either by continuous innovation in medical treatment and in methods of service delivery, or by rationing and the erosion of quality.

Rationing is an increasingly stark problem for government, and for individuals aware of treatments they cannot get and service deficits that surprise them. Immense opportunities for immediate patient benefit are being denied because of lack of funds. Many innovations are being unnecessarily rationed or delayed. Increases in productivity and wealth have generally arisen from technological change. This is vital in the NHS, which is labour intensive. Yet the NHS restricts investment, re-organisation, service development and productivity. New demand, which could be created and supplied in the private sector, is not allowed to occur in the public sector. It has been made difficult for resources (in often fossilised institutions) to move from the obsolete to the new as easily as possible, and for new forms of production to meet new forms of demand.

There are, visibly, in deficits and denials, grave contradictions between the theory of the NHS and its practice. These contradictions—rationing itself and the pleas for self-responsibility from government to patients—are rooted in the assumptions of the NHS. These assumptions misunderstand that moralising and morality have different roots. The NHS waiting lists are the most obvious sign of the accumulation of deficits and denials.

There is a Malthusian notion implicit in NHS thinking about rationing, too. This is that resources could never increase sufficiently to meet the growth in demand, and so prudent but bureaucratic rationing must be applied. Meanwhile, there are many occasions when NHS managers must feel like the Jumblies, in Edward Lear's poem, who went to sea in a sieve. A different reality, a different structure, more diverse funding, and greater self-responsibility are essential. To make this politically acceptable a new relationship between social and economic goals must be devised.

Meanwhile, the NHS remains outside the modernisation of the economy. In the wider economy there has been a general rise in real incomes. This has come from dramatic increases in productivity. We have seen the evolution of personalised, customized, responsive, competitive services. Here, innovation is constant and is secured by preferences, as the power of competition has unleashed innovation and unheard of rates of progress. Yet the NHS is the last, failed, nationalised industry. It remains, to borrow William Cowper's poetic terms, 'that reeling goddess with the zoneless waist'. It is cut off from what Michael Porter, the leading authority on strategy and competition, has called 'the five-forces framework'. This comprises the bargaining power of buyers, the bargaining power of suppliers, the threat of new entry, the threat of substitutes, and the intensity of rivalry. The NHS thus severs itself from the framework which is at the root of successful change. As Porter says:

> The environment, poverty, health care and income inequality are normally seen as social problems ...however, each of them is inextricably bound up with economics and, more specifically, with competition. Bringing a sophisticated understanding of competition to bear is not only revealing but offers concrete, workable approaches to solutions.[3]

The five forces generate increased productivity and long-term development. However, NHS institutions stand disconnected from this 'positioning', which would enable them to do better for their users by greater operational effectiveness or attainment of best practice. They disregard the value-chain which offers a systematic approach to examining what they do so as to achieve competitive advantage. Yet sustainable performance most often depends on having a distinctive strategic position. It is the alternative to the drive for top-down rationing, described by the government's chief economic adviser (Clive H. Smee) as 'improving the efficiency of the resource gap'.[4]

These understandings were excluded from the Conservative reforms of the early 1990s, as they are from the 'modernisation' proposed by the present government. Each of these series of changes has side-stepped the fundamental difficulties—by avoiding financial restructuring; by failing to give power to the individual patient; by sustaining block contracts; by failing to confront surprising variations in clinical practice; and by enabling local management to continue as no more than administration.[5] The NHS has remained captive in 'politics'. This has continued despite New Labour's own emphasis on competitive markets in all other sectors, even including education.

The concealment of price—which can signal both the shrinkage of customer groups and the emergence of a superior product or service—and the suppression of free markets ensures the denial of these fundamentals. The absence of appropriate information and of good communication, characteristic of the NHS, is one of the most serious consequences.

Much of this pattern of rejection is cultural and political. It seems increasingly clear, however, that the expectations of quantity, quality and access that people have of health care cannot be provided by a narrow funding base relying on tax income alone. The NHS falls short of what people living in a rich country expect. Health inequalities in the UK are considerable, and greater than in many countries which organise and fund health care differently. This, despite the promise of service 'free' at the point of delivery. The NHS does not ensure that all classes and all patient groups in each geographical region obtain equal access, equal utilisation of services, or optimal outcomes. There are, too, biases by gender and by age. In these vital senses the NHS fails *on its own terms* to secure 'fairness' (or equity), universality, comprehensiveness, and 'quality'.

These are the striking and explicit difficulties that are embedded in the rationed service. Government has entrenched the control of consumers by producers, and entrenched the monopoly of the relatively few suppliers. Government, too, has reinforced by its actions the difficulties of the poorly organised and poorly informed consumer. It has constrained the incentives to providers to demonstrate and improve the advantages of their services. A single-payer system, or public-sector monopoly, has limited services by deliberately constraining income and investment. It maintains closed entry to the professions, which tends to suppress competition, increase professional incomes, and limit the number of doctors. It limits information, too, withholding vital facts—as it must do if government is to curtail individual pressure and choice.

There is often patient ignorance of possibilities. This is not an accident. Much patient ignorance, for which patients are often blamed, arises from assumptions made by NHS professionals about the capacity of the individual and the potential of markets. People are not helped to learn to make choices, or to discriminate between risks and uncertainties. They are instead encouraged to under-value their own 'subjectivity'. They learn to be dependent, and not to educate themselves to escape from ignorance and to secure informed choice. Decisions, for which alternative choices exist, are often made—undiscussed—*for* individuals.

The issue of patient ignorance is important. Planners and professionals often point to this to justify the rationing process in which they alone claim to be competent to make decisions about scarce resources and between patients. However, it is the work-ings of the public-sector monopoly which *necessarily* limit the information available, and which discourage self-education in order to deter and to 'discipline' demand. It is difficult, for example, for patients to discover who undertakes a procedure frequently and successfully. Nor is information about drug treatments necessarily available. One health authority (hardly atypical) was recently reported to have a policy of limiting the prescription of the Alzheimer's drug Aricept by discouraging GPs from initiating or recommending treatment with the drug. The report said: 'Patients have to ask for it. Here is a case where patients with dementia have to remember the name of the drug before they can receive it'.[6] Patients who have to be reminded who they are have to take responsibility for reminding the GP to give them an effective drug!

One clinical analyst has recently pointed out that:

> Government provision also encourages ignorance. Private patients want to know what is done to them and private doctors want to keep their custom, so that gradually the whole community becomes better educated

in health care. Those who are interested learn what works and what does not. The remainder either follow their lead, or learn where to go for independent advice. Everyone becomes more demanding of good health care and more resistant to bad health propaganda. Public patients in contrast are supplicants to the doctor. They are reluctant to ask questions because they might upset their doctor, and he certainly doesn't volunteer information. Before long the community is so ignorant that providers can argue that people are not qualified to judge what they want for themselves.[7]

The NHS thus asks people to scale down their reasonable expectations. Its financial regime, too, deters people from investing their own money in what they want. Many people would like to spend more on health services, as the British Social Attitudes Survey indicates. Yet fewer than a third of those surveyed wanted taxes to rise to pay for it. Support for higher spending on health care falls if an increase in taxes is necessary to pay for it.[8]

The justification offered by government for present levels of spending is the claim that the UK spends less of its domestic product on health care than the OECD average; that it achieves at least average outcomes; that it achieves more than some countries who spend more; and that the NHS is therefore 'efficient'. This is, however, too general a claim. As I argue and illustrate, the claim relies on aggregate data which conceals varied outcomes. The NHS does not track patients to gather information on what has actually been achieved in effective outcomes, or what has worked for individuals over time. The assertion that the NHS is efficient implies a quality service to each individual. Yet the NHS, as we shall see, has many deficits and denials of services and of care to specific individuals and to entire classes of patients. There are many possible solutions which could address the difficulties, but these require leadership. The NHS, however, retains its power to impose a political price on change, and the political fear of public opinion has limited leadership. Opinion, too, has been misled by half a century of 'free' services.

In an open democracy it has been problematic for politicians to address these challenges. Politicians have feared the political risks of facing reality in health care. However, as John Wyndham commented in his *The Kraken Wakes*: 'If all the energy that is put into diddling mugs for their votes could be tuned on to useful work, what a nation we could be!'[9]

That useful work now requires a fundamental re-appraisal of the capacity, performance, financing and relationships of health care. It is become unavoidable. This is the consequence of a variety of internal and external pressures which identify the difficulties and which offer a contrast with the world outside the NHS.

The NHS, too, represents a wider difficulty for the economy as a whole. It offers an uncompetitive contradiction to the entrepreneurial values, behaviour and attitudes necessary in a more venturesome economy—one less regulated and less taxed, to encourage more individual freedom and competitive enterprise. It is a matter for speculation how long government can continue to spend the equivalent of 40 per cent of national income and hope to envisage a more dynamic economy. Here, what happens about health care is an important influence. For the NHS is the largest demander from a high-tax, high-spending public sector which raises prices, inflates the currency, and distorts international competitiveness. The commitment to a public-sector monopoly in health care hinders the necessary reduction of the share of individual income taken by the state. It hinders the positive performance of price and profit and their innovative power to help lift all boats. The impact of these attitudes, too, has had a significant impact on the quality of NHS management. This remains weak in infrastructure, human resource management, technological development and in procurement. Serious clinical deficiencies have remained unmanaged.

In contradiction of Porter's five forces for improvement, the politicisation of health care has consistently emptied NHS management of its essential roles. This has recently been described by Professor Alan Maynard as 'derisory', in failing to manage recruitment and retention of staff, of work-loads, skill-mix, and the 'enormous' variations in clinical activity and practice as well as necessary professional transformation in changing roles—all key to 'quality'. Management has been prevented from attracting and managing key factors—notably capital goods, nurses, hospital consultants and clinical performance. One consequence has been the maintenance of the culture of institutionalised hospital medicine—a factor in deterring recruitment and retention.[10] Waste, too, is very considerable, according to the government's own Audit Commission, notably in supplies management. The number of NHS Trusts failing to break even in 1997/98 rose to 33 per cent, and Trusts had a net deficit of £107 million in 1997/98, compared with £55 million in the previous year. However, since these are not under the imperative to deliver-or-go-bust (the normal incentive to respond to consumers' wishes) none do so.[11]

At the heart of these questions are huge issues: the fundamentals of human nature, the sources of responsibility and morality, the basis of prosperity, the relationship between the state and the individual, and our identity as a nation.

The realities of rationing in the NHS arise within a disciplined, centralised structure of public-sector near-monopoly. This is a system in which government has collaborated for its own purposes with professional bodies of organised medicine. It has empowered the producer, whilst disempowering demand. In Hayek's words, the NHS spares 'the susceptibilities of the mighty'.

The question of supply and demand is paramount, but it arises within philosophical and political contexts. The public policy issues raised by rationing are by no means confined to how to get more money into the system. Nor are they resolvable merely by spending 'sufficient' money. Nor can 'sufficient' be measured in the absence of price. There are apparently conflicting answers from the market and from politics. Can we resolve them?

# 2

# Re-defining Collectivism: Can Social and Economic Goals be Reconciled?

How can economic and social goals be reconciled, so that health care can benefit from the unique drives of competition, whilst contributing to social harmony? How can we reconcile the goals of personal freedom and social justice, broadening the funding and enhancing the capacity of health care whilst securing social harmony, self-responsibility and good cover for all? It seems at least possible, in part from observing contemporary European experience, that to base health care almost entirely on tax-based funding is not the only nor even the most likely way to achieve equity (in finance and in access) and optimal care. This, I argue, instead requires individual autonomy and self-responsibility, and the dynamics of a competitive market, within a structure which also obtains the social harmony of recognised equity and social solidarity. These questions concern how social policy makers see the market, and how free-marketeers see government interventionism. The conflict concerns means. The socialist effort to achieve social goals—by re-distribution, subsidy and rationing—fails because it misunderstands the springs of social and economic action. Even a commentator like the sociologist Anthony Giddens on the left has recognised that: 'Socialism also failed to grasp the significance of markets as informational devices, providing essential data for buyers and sellers'.[1] And: 'there are no alternatives to capitalism'.[2] Markets, too, can evidence failures. But these are our only mechanisms. Can a better balance be struck between government failure and market failure? How might economic and social goals be harmonised? Can the impulses of collectivism be re-defined, re-focused, for better health care?

Economic and social policy have been seen as distinct and often competing. Economic policy concerns itself with creating wealth from incentives, encouraging savings and investment and minimizing government intervention. Social policy, by contrast, has concentrated on providing 'public goods' by reliance on government intervention, subsidies, and redistribution.

Welfare thinkers see the market as the problem and attempt to modify its outcomes. Economic policy makers tend to see government intervention as the problem. Social advocacy groups often view business as the problem, whilst business leaders see social goals as outside their realm of interest. They view a strong economy, unshackled by counterproductive intrusions, as the best social programme.[3]

Porter may offer the answer. He suggests that it is possible to pursue both economic and social goals:

> This can be done through a central focus on innovation and competition—working through the market rather than against it. Social programs must prepare individuals to enter and succeed in the market system, not insulate them from it. Efforts to address social issues, such as pollution and the high costs of health care, must harness innovation and competition to address underlying causes, rather than attempt to shift the costs onto some other group within society.[4]

Our failure to benefit from hard thinking about these issues creates our difficulties. Fundamental to this failure has been the antipathy to competition and to profit, even though NHS Trusts did £288 million of private work in 1997/98, and despite the clear fact that revolutionary changes in living standards arise from competition. Unless competition is harnessed within health care, the patient will continue to take the strain in a seller's market where people are limited to what state financing can provide.

We *can* find ways to combine social and economic goals, but competition must be freed. Otherwise, neither are achievable. As Porter and colleagues say:

> The answer lies in the powerful lessons business has learned over the past two decades about the imperatives of competition. In industry after industry, the underlying dynamic is the same: competition compels companies to deliver increasing value to customers. The fundamental driver of this continuous quality improvement and cost reduction is

innovation. Without incentives to sustain innovation in health care, short-term cost savings will soon be overwhelmed by the desire to widen access, the growing health needs of an aging population, and the unwilling-ness...to settle for anything less than the best treatments available. Inevitably, the failure to promote innovation will lead to lower quality or more rationing of care—two equally undesirable results.[5]

The NHS system lacks these compulsions. The collectivised NHS approach to health care has not produced a comprehensive, universally accessible system. Nor one with sufficient funding or capacity to meet modern demands. The system is not free, nor equal, and no one has a right to treatment. The NHS is thus unresponsive to consumers; it remains tailored to the producer rather than the consumer. Vital areas are under-served. The chief executive of the NHS Confederation (representing NHS Trusts and Health Authorities) recently stated that cancer care in Britain is haphazard and inadequate, and that mental health services are in a deplorable state.[6] Politics causes much of this state-induced rationing. For example it is a major dilemma, for health authority purchasers struggling with insufficient budgets, whether or not to fund the treatment of a disease where the outcome is often and predictably death—for example, with the three most common tumour types, breast cancer, lung and colorectal cancer. These, too, are amongst the most resistant to chemotherapy. Spending on chemo agents in the UK only accounts for one per cent of the total NHS drug spend. In addition, the licensed introduction of new and more expensive cytotoxics into hospital use are often for the end stages of disease when all previous therapies have failed and where the patient's life expectancy is reduced. Who is to decide that a dying patient should not be given a costly drug which might give him or her another year of useful life, and on which grounds?[7]

Within a system of state-rationed 'needs' patients and profess-ionals find they are, necessarily, in a beggar-my-neighbour situation. In a system of limited funding, if one patient does better another must be the loser, for example, in the competition for resources both between differing cancer patients and between cancer care and other specialisms such as cardiovascular disease, diabetes and chronic problems of old age. Many professionals are uncomfortable in having to make rationing decisions which conflict with professional ethical principles concerning the patient presenting for treatment.

Meanwhile, the consumer faces the inherent difficulties of uncertainty about the necessity and efficacy of treatments and the competence of practitioners. Consumers, too, are little conscious of cost, since the incentive in a 'free' system—when they are not directly spending their own money—is to demand more. This has not, however, delivered quite basic standards.

A key difficulty is that there is no incentive to personal responsibility in self-care, or to cost-conscious behaviour. Instead, rationing by officials and professionals is given parity of moral esteem with self-responsible choice. This is a false idea. It displaces self-responsible choice. Allocative rationing limits individuals to that 'positive liberty' described by Isaiah Berlin—that enforced self-realisation determined by the state, which obstructs choice. This by contrast with the 'negative' liberty of the autonomous, self-responsible individual in a pluralist society which Berlin offered as the fullest realisation of a human being.[8]

There are many denials to patients who could otherwise benefit from treatments that could be readily available. These costs involve much increased pain, suffering and disability. The myth of 'free' services—with its many negative incentives—is increasingly transparent to the disappointed individual. Health care is regularly 'reformed' (or reconstructed) administratively. But we await the most essential reform. This is that the concerned individual consumer can escape to a preferred provider. We know the economic mechanisms which could achieve this. We need the political courage to finesse change across all classes. Then leveraged choice can be available to all. The most important contribution government can make to better health care is to allow the freedom of experiment and the personal gauging of risk, based on adequate information at the level of *specific* treatments from *specific* providers. This is essential for the expression of preference and its financial empowerment.

The NHS has inadequate finance with which to meet the opportunities and demands of patients for modern health services. The politicised nature of the NHS is at the root of the problem, for government deliberately determines the limits of funding. These systemic problems are only correctable if the source of funds is more diverse and capacity much greater. The moral issue of how to achieve self-responsibility can only be addressed if purchasing power is transferred to the individual.

Essentially, the problem is about what kind of society we wish to live in, what potential we believe individuals have and can develop. In the necessary programme of change, we have to begin from where we are. The political challenge is how to finesse change, to shift the institutional framework, which is respected and held in affection by the public but which has serious deficits in funding, capacity and morality.

Rationing implicates the NHS in fundamental challenges which are pivotal to the cultural nature of public policy. The realities of rationing go beyond whether or not a service can be obtained, and whether it is appropriate and cost-effective. The basis on which judgements are made has implications concerning morality, self-responsibility and liberty, as well as for which services are available, to whom and where. These issues raise fundamental questions about philosophy and objectives. For rationing reveals basic questions about the state, politics and power, morality and liberty. These are political, economic, philosophical and moral questions.

The strictly economic benefits of competition are a gain, but they are not the only gain. The chief benefit is to express a particular philosophy about 'character' and human nature, about the manner of human association, about the appropriate role of government.

It is a major question how equality of access to good care can be achieved in practice, rather than only in theory, as it is in the present NHS. The proper objective is to meet the social goal of universal cover, but within an innovative market where individuals take moral responsibility for living their own lives. To achieve this we need to openly admit the importance of emotion, if we are to address and re-assure the key fears of many—what happens to the elderly or the poor as changes come and for whom advocacy may be weak? Financial mobility and individual leverage (or private property rights) are *both* vital, especially for the poor, if they are to acquire the power the non-poor enjoy now.

It is vital that all have good health cover. It is imperative that the poor and chronically sick are included. There must be a moral minimum commitment to provision that is at least as good as present provision. That is, there must be a guarantee by government that there will be good quality basic care available to all—and at least as good as is available now. There must be freedom of choice, and competitive pricing to ensure efficiency and appropriate allocation of scarce resources in response to purchasing contracts willingly entered into. This could be guaranteed by risk-adjusted insurance contracts (or personally-vested, portable and tax-exempt medical savings accounts). A possible model is that of Singapore, which is based on individual responsibility, buttressed by a government subsidy to ensure coverage for all. The Medisave scheme requires all working individuals to make co-payments, to meet part of all costs. They may elect for additional services, for a fee. Contributions are mandatory, tax-exempt, and cumulate whilst earning interest. Unspent monies credited to individuals are carried forward as family savings. Catastrophic illness is covered by Medishield insurance. The poor are covered by the Medifund scheme, paid for by government.[9] People are then free to rise above the minimum guaranteed by the state, to invest their own resources, if they so choose. There is no intrinsic reason why some people being willing to spend their money to exercise choice must inevitably leave those who cannot afford to make such choices worse off.

It is not as if the poor and the sick necessarily do well in the NHS now. The NHS stresses 'fairness' but does not achieve it. For here, as one doctor has commented (he is discussing the medical problems of the elderly):

> People with wealth, social standing, education, and the ability to appeal to the media will work the system to get the care they need. The poor, the uneducated and the socially disadvantaged will bear most of the burden of the limited resources...[10]

This is a two-tier system, offending against both morality and efficiency. Equality of access has appeared as a precise and definite statement to justify the NHS public-sector monopoly and a narrow financial base, but it has proved ambiguous, vague, and imprecise. It has been a legal and a romantic fiction.

People want health services to work well, and they want them to come into line with their modern experiences of other services, competitively provided. But, understandably, too, they want painless change, impossible as this is. Change is both necessary and unavoidable. For competitive services to emerge, for this to be politically acceptable, for people to have time to adjust, change will need to be gradual and incremental, a shift over a generation or more. It is crucial to be very aware of emotions, as it is to put in place something better. The process of change will necessarily be profoundly unsettling. But a start is essential if insufficiency and inefficiency are to be addressed. As we re-assess the failings of the NHS—the realities revealed by rationing—we need to re-consider the impulses of 'collectivism'. We need to see how economic and social goals can be reconciled. That is, we need to respond to the public affection for the epic solace of the NHS but to correct its intimate disappointments. This is to re-define the basis of services to ensure both that there is a safety net and a strong sense of responsibility. We need to ensure, too, that there is sufficient money and capacity for modern health services. We need to re-examine how we can get higher quality, lower cost, sensitive and personalised services.

These are the daily cultural, political, financial and service realities of NHS rationing. We need to seek common civic ground (and political acceptability) by re-defining collectivism—to offer individual ownership *within* collective provision. A solution would be the empowerment of mutual aid as an alternative to state dominance of purchasing and provision, whilst protecting the weak.

In asking such questions—the words are those of the poet and publisher John Lehmann—we need to be the 'hunter of living truth through the forests of seeming'.[11] We need to examine the genuine processes of discovery and development. We need to examine the detailed realities of rationing, its philosophy, assumptions, derivation, and results.

The government regulates the private sector heavily, on the assumption that public is better than private. This idea is justified principally on political grounds (but stated ethically) concerning equality and re-distribution. This process has the curiously paradoxical result of increasing selfishness, for it makes of politics a mechanism for profit at the expense of others. What has happened in practice is that measures designed to help the minority poor (and the chronically sick) have harmed them by making them compete with the majority non-poor for the rationed and restricted supplies made available by the state.[12]

Notably, those with low incomes have done least well in a price-less system. The NHS has re-distributed opportunities in favour of the middle class. The cash-limited public-sector monopoly is necessarily a zero-sum game of beggar-my-neighbour. For, in a system cash-limited from above, if one individual gains an advantage—by class, by connections, by pressure or by choices expressed by clinicians—this must be at the expense of someone else. The gain must detract from the total resources available, and no benefit is conferred on the whole, unlike in competitive markets where demand ratchets up investment and service.

Nature does ration each of us, but we need not make things worse. Nor should we live unaware of others. We should keep in mind Thackeray's words on this Vanity Fair in which we live:

> The hidden and awful Wisdom which apportions the destinies of mankind is pleased so to humiliate and cast down the tender, good, and wise; and to set up the selfish, or foolish, or the wicked. Oh be humble, my brother in your prosperity! Be gentle with those who are less lucky, if not more deserving. Think, what right have you to be scornful, whose virtue is a deficiency of temptation, whose success may be a chance, whose rank may be an ancestor's accident, whose prosperity is very likely a satire.[13]

### What We Spend: A European Comparison

Britain is near the bottom of the league table in spending on health services as a percentage of gross domestic product (GDP). State spending is much the same throughout western Europe. The difference between us and most European countries is that our private sector spend is low. It is a well acknowledged picture: we spend some 5.8 per cent of GDP from taxation and some 1.1 per cent of private income. This compares with a European average of 7.7 per cent and an OECD average of 10.4 per cent.

In Germany, 10.4 per cent of GDP is spent on health care, but only 14 per cent of this total expenditure comes from government. In Holland, 8.8 per cent of GDP is spent, but only 10 per cent of this comes from taxation. Elsewhere, too, the sources of funding are many. The USA spends 14.1 per cent, but there is disagreement about the level of 'benefit' derived. However, it seems clear that in many specialist areas—such as cancer, coronary heart disease and schizophrenia—a greater spend has solid results. For example, it helps fund more doctors in training. In the UK there is a serious shortage of doctors and a high level of deaths from cancer. The UK is in the highest group of countries for occurrence and deaths. Investment, too, is only slowly being made in specialist centres and increased training, and at a lower rate than in many European countries.

The International Congress on Anti-Cancer Treatment, held in Paris on 4 February 1999, was advised that deaths from cancer in the UK could be reduced. This could be achieved if funding improved, more was spent on drugs, more specialists were appointed, and services were better co-ordinated. Britain does poorly in each of these key areas. There are too few 'one stop' shops, too few patients recruited into clinical trials, and waiting lists are too long. Again, the European comparisons hurt. France spends three times as much per head on cancer drugs as Britain, and Germany twice as much. Survival rates for every form of cancer except for skin cancer are higher in America, too, than in any European country. In Switzerland, for example, a colon cancer patient has a 51 per cent chance of surviving for five years. In the UK that figure is 36 per cent, while in America it is as high as 60 per cent. Five-year survival rates for breast cancer, according to the World Health Organisation, are at 82 per cent for America, 75 per cent in Finland and 63 per cent in Britain.

Britain lags behind other nations in cutting cancer death rates. We spend a total of £55 million a year treating cancer. This is a tenth of spending, in absolute terms, on cancer drugs in America. These inadequate levels of funding, experts were told, have an impact on survival rates. Mortality could clearly be reduced further using currently available interventions, techniques and knowledge. Funding has increased recently, with an additional £10 million to be spent on breast cancer and a further £10 million on colo-rectal cancer services. A broader base of funding in the NHS would dramatically alter this still inadequate situation.[14]

However, in the NHS the proportion of the health spend covered from taxation (some 84 per cent) has remained at a consistent level even after 18 years in which Conservative administrations were in power and gave at least some encouragement for private provision.

The difference (or deference) between Britain and the rest of the developed world is that the independent spend on health care in the UK is very little. A direct result is the insufficient competitive provision we confront. Another result is serious skills shortage. Britain has the fewest doctors per head of population amongst the countries of Europe, apart from Albania and Turkey. We have the fewest nurses and dentists per head in Western Europe. For example, in Finland there are 2,130 trained nurses for every 100,000 of population; in Britain there are 450. Britain, too, has high rates of infections acquired while in hospital, yet employs relatively few infection control nurses. It was recently reported that as many as 70,000 patients a year develop a life-threatening illness, are left with a severe disability, or die as a direct result of being in hospital.[1b] Britain is only the fourteenth healthiest nation among the 35 countries of Europe.

The Nordic countries do well because they have developed good community medicine. It is a key deficit in the NHS that this has proved very difficult to achieve in the UK. This is in part because of the political power of the hospitals (and of hospital consultants) as social and political institutions in a politicised NHS. This difficulty has increased, as NHS Hospital Trusts—in a political market-place—have expanded their power to obstruct local change, relying on location and on political clout. They often command the purchasing authority, rather than the reverse. One serious consequence is the inadequacy of support in the community for ill and elderly patients. Here, hospital discharge policy often serves patients less than helpfully. There are crude definitions of 'independent living'. As one senior NHS manager said to me recently: 'If an elderly lady can stand up, put her knickers on, and make a cup of tea she can be discharged. Never mind if she falls over on the way home, or can hardly cook for herself when she gets there'. This anecdotal evidence is confirmed by patients who reported to the Audit Commission that they believed they were often discharged too soon, and in pain.[16]

Even so, in Britain health care spending is at record levels: some £42 billion this year, compared with £433 million at the outset of the NHS in 1948. However, health care is provided only sparingly by international standards. Spending has not kept up with demand. Waiting lists remain significant. They result from the way care is financed and organised—the 'under-funding' commonly denounced by pressure-group bidders. 'Under-funding' is, of course, an accusation with no meaning, since the proposed additional marginal utility is never tested in a competitive market.

Britain has not grown a private health care sector of comparable size to most similar European countries, nor has it developed charging for specifics, except at the margin. However, those European nations which have done so show much less inequality in the health of their citizens. One analyst, John Willman, offers the interesting observation that 'failing to impose charges distorts choice'. He suggests that paying does not necessarily lead to greater inequality; that most European states require some payments; that charges may reduce demand for 'unnecessary' usage; and that the 'sick poor' can be protected by targeted measures.[17] These arguments apply equally to insurance, which need not necessarily be a worst-case solution, and which would address many deficits. It may prove to be the case, too, that being in a market is itself educational, and that people whose self-esteem increases by making learned decisions do see their health improve. A shift in emphasis might, too, help us move away from the medical model, which over-emphasises 'treatment' and under-emphasises personal responsibility, self-esteem, self-control, and lifestyle issues like diet, exercise, and non-smoking. For research has shown that investment in hospitals has not been the most important determinant of changes in health status.[18] Charging itself, however, has only limited value: it increases revenues and encourages some price-conscious demand, but it does not create the mobility of finance in the hands of an individual which would energise the framework of competition offered by Porter.

## Who Should Decide Who Decides? Fortifying Demand and Recovering Price

All governments accept that health care is necessarily rationed. There is a genuine debate about who should decide on the principles of health care rationing, how should rationing be done, and by whom? The issue, as one experienced and innovative patient-centred NHS manager has put it, is 'who decides who decides?', on what basis and for which public and private purposes?[19]

The key question is, who is to do the rationing? Should it be done by government, at the level of general taxation and by contract at the local level through GPs organised in primary care groups and health authorities? Or by patients themselves, as patient fundholders or insured individuals, gathered voluntarily in not-for-profit community organisations of mutual aid? This would be to re-define 'collectivism' in a non-alien way which has direct roots in Labour's own traditions. It would recognise the old working-class wish to 'get on', too, in bold but temperate self-reliance and independent judgement. These are traditions which have been muted and buried by decades of centralisation, but they offer great potential to combine economic and social goals.[20]

The most significant loss in 1948 was the suppression of the price mechanism. Those on the left take the view that price means no choice for some, but the opposite is true, for it is possible to reinforce the buying power of those with lower-incomes by tax-transfers. This would give their wishes an equivalent weight with those middle-class competitors who best them in the NHS. Priced demand also uniquely unveils the processes of discovery in the economy. For competition, of course, offers a unique discovery procedure, to reveal preference, to co-ordinate cost-conscious choice, to measure demand and allow the free expression of the self-responsible individual. The denial of this essential is the reason that self-responsibility is so difficult to achieve in a paternalist system. The planner instead assumes the possibility of omniscience and ubiquity in planning, as a substitute for price as the basis of understanding. However, planning in health care is not an intelligible economic instrument. It is a political instrument. It produces shortages *in itself*.

A key issue is the question of provision for those on low incomes, who would have difficulty paying for themselves even if there were an insurance system and group provision. Special arrangements must be made. In the NHS, however, the political device of 'free' supply has turned out to be a false solution to supplying services for those on low incomes. The better solution would have been not to erase the price barrier and lose the essential information which only markets collect and reveal, but to retain charges while providing funding for those least able to pay them. This would have retained self-responsibility and the ability to express preferences, while at the same time enabling those individuals who could do so to contribute more (as they do in Europe).

The necessity now is to strengthen the power of the individual consumer by fortifying demand and offering tax-incentives to increase personal spending. This would enable us to fortify demand for those defined as being in absolute poverty by revenue transfers, which could only be spent on health care purchases. Those on low incomes would receive subsidies, like the weighted voucher proposed by Julian Le Grand. Here, as in Switzerland, the government would remain the insurer of last resort, ensuring access for the poor and ultimately for the uninsured.[21] Such a tax-transfer would depend on personal situation and family size and the 'applicable amount' would take account of claimants and dependants. This is, also, the only route to give the individual dominance over producers in the market process, and over politicians in the political process. We might then (and only then) sort out preferences, identify priorities, encourage additional resources and responsive provision, and re-build personal responsibility.

We must give new life to the lessons learned in order to bring together the moral objectives, the health objectives, and the economic objectives of society. For the political control and provision of health care in a public-sector monopoly has been deeply damaging. It has worsened the funding and provision of intimate personal services, and intruded harmfully on our character. Government has made the problems much worse than they need be.

# 3

# The Three Principal Problems: Finance, Capacity, and Self-responsibility

The lynch-pin of the three problems of finance, capacity and self-responsibility is the lack of competition.

The cultural, operational and fiscal deficits so visible now in the NHS are thus no accident. They are a direct and explicit consequence of government decisions to limit funding in the main to taxation, to hinder the development of alternative funding mechanisms and to deter competitive provision. The solution is the systematic introduction of clear, competitive market incentives so that health care has access to the dramatic improvements that are possible. Innovations that arise from competitive forces can bring health costs down without rationing services from above, by increasing investment in higher quality services. The necessary elements are six:

- Positive incentives to encourage competitive provision
- The development of an insurance system to encourage efficiency
- Full information about outcomes to ensure meaningful choice
- Individual financial leverage
- Positive attitudes towards risk-taking and innovation to ensure dynamic improvement
- Compliance with modern standards of delivery

This echoes Porter's 'five-forces framework'. It will ensure the bargaining power of buyers, the bargaining power of suppliers, the threat of new entry, the threat of substitutes, and the intensity of rivalry. These are the basis of effective, innovative competition to serve the consumer.

Absolutely basic is information. This should be at the level of *specific treatments* by *specific providers*, with data on long-term outcomes and immediate results. Then treatment outcomes and prices can guide choices. Investment in this information and its open publication is essential. So, too, is the certainty that sub-standard providers will exit. Purchasing pressures must endorse, reward and encourage faith in innovation and in competitive development.

Governments, of all parties, have prevented this structure from emerging. They have done so for reasons of ideology and political opportunism (equality; fairness; re-distribution; self-interest; timidity; the necessity to survive in office; re-election). Further-more, because governments prefer to run systems with well organised professionals and managers, the consumer has been marginalised. The 'public choice' (or Virginia) school of economists has analysed this phenomenon of the self-interested impulses of government (which sets the financial limits), and of the profes-sionals and managers (who distribute the scarce goods). The consumer, scattered and unorganised, remains on the margin.[1] Many in the NHS know that they wrestle with inconsolable difficulties within this structure, but they do not face the prob-lems of capacity and finance because they do not properly define them.

There are three principal problems in the NHS: finance, capacity and self-responsibility. They arise from the denials of the structure I have described. Each offers a cultural, a political, a moral, and an operational challenge.

### *The First Principal Problem is Finance*

Here, we are the odd man out in Europe, and further afield, in the amount available and the narrowly-based source of funds. The European health care consumer has more choice, more diverse provision, and is better funded.

There are a number of policy alternatives concerning the funding problem: to increase taxes (including hypothecation, or an assigned revenue dedicated to a specific purpose); to increase charging; to give incentives for personal insurance and to lower taxes; or to remain at present funding levels and enhance efficiencies. We could aim for a blend of tax-base and insurance, in which there were guarantees of service and freedom (as in New Zealand) to opt for state or private cover.[2]

We need to study Europe, and pay less attention to scare stories about the USA, which may or may not be justified or relevant. As we consider alternative funding structures, we need to be clear that the USA is not the only alternative. We can decide our own future, and learn from the gains and losses elsewhere. It is not inevitable that the poor be denied service. Faulty incentives which improve quality but which increase costs can be avoided.

Government should establish a new general legal framework, within which practice and service negotiation between providers and group purchasers would operate on behalf of individual 'patient fundholders'. There are valuable European examples, notably in the mixed markets and more transparent insurance systems of Germany and Holland, or Singapore on such issues as models of insurance, open enrolment, the blend of *individual* responsibility and subsidy, co-payment, and the maintenance of appropriate competition for patients to benefit from suitable incentives. A revolution in managed care need not necessarily skew incentives towards exclusions and poor quality, nor encourage supplier-induced demand. The problem of moral hazard—where there are no incentives for patients or doctors to restrain treatment—can be addressed directly (for example, by co-payments), as can adverse selection, or 'skimming', by regulation. Mandatory insurance can ensure that no-one is under-insured. We can be aware of the risks that new barriers to innovation can arise. We do not necessarily have to adopt destructive price rivalry. We can ensure that all are covered, there would be open enrolment, including those with pre-existing conditions. Those already in long-term care, in mental health, or in elderly care would be covered. Special transitional arrangements (within the funding regime) would be necessary for the elderly to ensure cover and care. There would be life-long cover, and risk equalisation among insurers. There would need, too, to be an arrangement for exceptional medical expenses (as in Holland), so that the 'rule of rescue' will not be breached and so that every individual would know with certainty what their contract entitled them to receive.

However, additional funding should come into the system via mechanisms other than expanding NHS budgets, if competitive incentives and genuine management are to emerge in the interests of patients.

We need not necessarily expand defensive medicine, nor over-treat or under-treat. Reimbursement need not inevitably be perverse, nor competition necessarily drive up costs, provided there is vigorous competition between both providers and payers to secure the allegiance of the individual. We need not inevitably increase the rate of recurrent or prolonged health problems because of economic incentives. We can be aware of the conflicting interests of payers, patients and providers. We can align payers' and patients' incentives. We can be alert to all these possibilities, account for them, and consciously design an alternative structure which will resolve many difficulties, as in Singapore.

### The Second Principal Problem is Insufficient Capacity

This is no accident. It is not incidental. It is a direct consequence of the reliance on state funding, and the hindering of the private sector. The deficits are very considerable, often startlingly so. The NHS lags behind other OECD countries in technology and service at many key junctures, despite high tax-costs and tight regula-tion.

In the UK, as we have seen, government deliberately places limits on health care spending. First, at the level of fiscal provi-sion. Then by a variety of devices to deter demand. It sets priorities amongst those services or treatments which could be provided. It curbs costly care by fiscal controls and by scarcity of supply. It supports rationing in many (often arbitrary and ad hoc) forms: by prioritisation and exclusion, by restricted direct access and by queue, by charging, by purchaser contracts which set upper limits on the numbers of routine operations performed, and by likelihood of benefit (a doctor's decision). It sets priorities, too, by the predilection of the provider, by time restriction, by sup-pressing information, and by a standard of service, a standard of built environment, and a tolerance of attitudes which themselves deter. It rations, too, by minimal provision of services such as psychiatry; by limiting expensive drugs or particular treatments;

by restricting investment in medical manpower and in the built environment; by discounting complementary forms of treatment such as aromatherapy, acupuncture, holistic and herbal medicines.

Much of this is a surprise to people who suddenly become 'a patient' after a healthy life. It is a shock to the growing numbers of sufferers from chronic long-term conditions, and to those with mental health difficulties. Many patients only discover the realities of rationing when they are in a relatively late stage of the treatment of a condition. Rationing exists on many different levels. It limits more than drugs or visits to clinics. It hinders pain management, the development of appropriate palliative care, and even a patient's control over an easeful and contented death.[3]

Thus, we notice what Milton Friedman called 'government failure' (whose external effects are generally under-estimated, and which are the hardest to correct, as governments buy votes). This contrasts with 'market failure' (which is over-estimated, usually for political purposes).

We should remind ourselves that a market need not be perfect in order to be superior to no market. However, by denying this the NHS itself has represented an enormous opportunity cost for society as a whole. The argument here is that the political supply of health care and its rationing mechanisms has damaged the evolution of quality services. These could have evolved at lower cost from alternative suppliers. These concealed costs of the failures in capacity include the ('counter-factual') alternatives. These were developing with distinct advantages before the Second World War, and could have been more satisfactorily supported in a more diverse and competitive structure. In the 1940s the UK could have continued to develop a modern system based on diverse sources of funding and on competitive provision. This could have been the continuing locale for individual subscription on a voluntary basis, in the indigenous mutual aid organisations and voluntary bodies to which people willingly committed themselves and their families. These were not profit-led organisations, although profits were achieved and distributed to members—as lower costs or greater benefits—as a result of organisation and pressure on providers.

They still have the potential to bring the pressures of local opinion, local ambitions, and local vision to bear upon services and their local development. These organisations have much to offer in a new relationship between government, business, and other local institutions. They have, too, the moral and intellectual features of individualism, freedom, enterprise, choice, initiative and competition. They imply a small apparatus of the state.

Historical study suggests that had mutual aid organisations continued to build after the 1940s the access of the poor to better care could have been very different. These spontaneous and characteristically British, non-political, voluntarist, intermediary and mutual aid organisations arose in a huge variety in the nineteenth century. They exercised a moral role in civilising and socialising individuals, who rationed for themselves and made individual decisions as moral beings.[4]

These were the home and school of Shirley Letwin's 'vigorous virtues', the development of the faculties of the individual, the virtues of 'character' and self-help—for the artisan as well as for the middle class. Alan Duncan and Dominic Hobson call mutual aid organisations 'the private schools of virtue'.[5] They were the route to growth of the individual, to self-respect and to an active, morally well-founded concern for others.

J.S. Mill made the case, concerned as he was with the 'vigorous exercise of the active energies' for the development of individual judgement and self-control. These were uniquely developed, in his view, by the individual confronting the difficulties of life, and by making choices which also contributed to a check on over-powerful government.

### The Third Principal Problem is Self-responsibility

This, government seeks to encourage—albeit on the narrow footing of 'responsible consumption' (or 'efficient resource utilisation'). However, the assumptions, structure and purposes of the NHS make even this limited objective difficult if not impossible to achieve. For the NHS has suppressed the true sources of morality, to which it can no longer appeal. The corrective is to encourage the moral, self-directed individual—the author of his or her own life—to take responsibility, to endeavour to be a better person.

There are two points here. First, self-responsibility in health care is necessarily an economic relationship—although liberty is much more than a market economy. Second, there can, indeed, be no responsibility without control.

Self-responsibility cannot be 'delivered' under the leadership of the state. For, as Berlin has argued, liberty is not achievable by imposition of so-called 'positive' liberty. The necessity is for 'negative' liberty, which rests on personal responsibility, on individual virtue and duty, and on non-political solidarity. These are the moral characteristics nourished most successfully in the family and in voluntary associations. These encourage virtue, which is displaced by the state and its professional clients in Friedman's 'iron triangle', where the emphasis has been on medical autonomy—with little managerial control and with patient empowerment disregarded.[6]

J.S. Mill and David Hume addressed these issues. Mill wrote that: 'A government cannot have too much of the kind of activity which does not impede but aids and stimulates exertion and development'. But he warned: 'The mischief begins when, instead of calling forth the activity and powers of individuals and bodies, it substitutes its own activity for theirs'.[7] Hume said that it is only the individual choosing freely to do what he wishes with his own money who can be making moral choices.[8]

The corollary is that a reduction of state welfare and the expansion of true responsibility is the pre-requisite for the moral regeneration of the individual, and for more meaningful care for the less fortunate.

# 4

# From a 1940s Mind-set To A Different World

Where did these realities of NHS rationing come from? Rationing and scarcity were emergency war-time experiences. In the echo of this world the NHS was established as a structure of institutionalised scarcity. This it has remained, although everything else in life has responded to markets.

Rationing and scarcity were part of the collective action of the national will to win a war against totalitarianism. But this world is long gone. Fair shares for all, in a backs-to-the-wall society, was a unifying cry. The Dunkirk spirit urged that the same rules applied to everyone. Collective buying and selling (in closed shops) was, too, the basis of the post-war consensus. This was a continuing drab world of uniformity where individuality was compulsorily subjected to the national effort to re-build. This produced an economy where one-size-fits-nobody. The assumption was that the functioning of the whole would be in the interests of the individual. Even in leisure, in holiday camps, this attitude prevailed. Now, it has gone, except in the NHS.

The NHS meets the classic prescription for undermining an enterprise by depriving it of the incentive and the opportunity to improve. It is an approach to health care which is as much theological as it is economic. There have been, from the beginning, difficulties about its intentions as well as about its effects. Subsequently, too, serious queries about the path taken by the nation—the path of welfare rather than of capital investment —have been offered by economists and others. The unwillingness to take risks, to accept personal responsibility, to expand the economy and to be more productive has been culturally pivotal. One consequence has been to restrict the creation of wealth (while contributing to inflation), thus restricting funds available for assisting the weaker to independently strengthen themselves.[1]

The context within which the 'visionary' ideas of William Beveridge were formulated and can be considered has altered rapidly in the recent past. The country is three times richer than it was in 1940. The proportion of manual workers has fallen from nearly two-thirds to less than half. The social condition of people in class five has dramatically shifted. Home ownership has more than doubled, being now close to 60 per cent. The expectations of the consumer are dramatically different. People have provided themselves in the market-place with entirely different lives: with houses, food, clothing, cars, consumer goods, foreign holidays, education. All this is due to innovations and productivity increases. This suggests, too, that the absolutely poor are fewer than many assume, and that the willingness to pay for what people want is both under-estimated and productive.

Family expenditure patterns illustrate this point. An average household spends more than £700 on TV, video and other entertainments. Sky, the satellite television service, costs more than £500 a year, over and above the £200 set-up cost for the magic box. Tobacco consumption costs the household with smokers an average exceeding £800 per annum. More than a quarter of households have a computer, eight in ten a video recorder, and a fifth a mobile telephone. Britain's illegal drugs trade, too, is estimated to be worth £8.5 billion, according to the Office for National Statistics. These are all comments on personal buying power in the economy, the latter a shocking statistic. [2]

At all events, the NHS has avoided the modernisation of the surrounding economy, which has customised service and encouraged effective demand. By contrast—and at a time when medicine can do more—the NHS struggles hard to *deter* demand, curtail supply, and discourage the consumer. This is in contrast to other areas of life where private endeavour adds energy, drive, investment, optimism, improved services, and a responsiveness that comes from a necessary sense of organisational jeopardy. By contrast, where there is no exit to alternatives outside the NHS, there are no choices other than to wait in hope or to do without.

Yet expectations of health care are changing as people become accustomed to choice and to high standards in every area of their lives. The context for public services has suddenly shifted from the memory of the 1930s and the centralising response of the 1940s to the post-modern consciousness of the informed consumer. We have seen the globalisation of information and of shared patient-experience, as the Internet personalises the rationing dilemma. We have seen, too, radically shifting expectations about relationships with professionals. The pressures on resources have multiplied and intensified as the result of technology and the successes of medicine itself. These factors, taken together, intensely query the ability and the legitimacy of government—as financier, planner, and controller of services. They re-focus, too, the potential of the individual for self-reflective, self-responsible health care and for cost-conscious choice.

The problems become greater, and of a different kind, when we consider genetic analysis and therapies. For the age of mass medicine is now confronted with the particular: the targeting of specific genes for specific conditions, and a revolutionary new personalised diagnosis. The pressures to intervene very early in the process of our natural history will be immense. The moral, fiscal, and medical questions are both enthralling and alarming. As Marshall Marrinker has said, 'the boundary between being a person and being a patient quite disappears'.[3] The nature of diagnosis and the specificity of treatment change, as, crucially, do the concepts of risk, probability and precautionary practice.

America's National Human Genome Research Institute expects the three-billion 'letter' human genetic code—the genome—to be deciphered by 2003. Our genetic individuality and pre-dispositions will then be demonstrated explicitly, and will be amenable to highly specific interventions.[4] The opportunities will be considerable, and many hundreds of conditions will become treatable in new ways. However, some costs will fall, if normal function can be restored in such congenital diseases as cystic fibrosis, although new cost opportunities will also emerge. Who will decide who should get what?

### Who the NHS Thinks We Are: Our Roles and Expectations

Enoch Powell, as textual critic, warned us to look beneath the surface, that 'in saying here is a stone, let us see what is behind the stone'. And: 'I am conscious that I have a habit of saying: "This isn't bloody well good enough. Therefore it cannot be right"'.[5] So we should notice and query many assumptions that are made by the NHS and its advocates. These are regarded as 'obvious'. The NHS is under-pinned by many often unstated assumptions—about human nature and character, about the manner of our association with one another, and about the appropriate role of government. These we need first to watch for, notice, and question.

One aggrandised assumption offers the notion that it is uniquely the role of government to be compassionate; that government should (and can) achieve equality and 'fairness'; that government is the source of the springs of duty and of personal morality. That public is more moral than private. Thus, the state should decide upon the level of health care funding.

This argument depends on the idea that all health services are necessarily 'public goods'. But this is both false and problematic. Much health care concerns lifestyle choices, and decisions about levels of preferred personal consumption for non-emergency, non-life-threatening interventions. Much is not necessarily a function of the state. Misunderstanding here has misled people to accept that health care can only be provided by the state.

There are two other ideas which reinforce this idea of command. One suggests that individuals need to be supervised, in their best interests. The other assumes that individual, and often conflicting, preferences can be aggregated into a planning decision. This planning assumption is predicated on the basis that price is unnecessary as a discovery process, and that cost-consciousness is not a matter for the individual. Instead, the state offers the political idea that elections and policy 'consultation' by health authorities are a genuine process of discovery about personal, intimate benefits, and that officials should make choices. This is a cluster of proposals which are disputable but too little discussed, as is the idea that it is wrong to make a profit from delivering a health service. It is especially doubtful that planners can know all relevant data in advance, or that they can adjust it efficiently by 'consultation'. On this last point, it was Mr. Holmes who remarked to Dr. Watson—the author himself was once a GP—that it is 'a capital mistake to theorise before one has data'. But planners must do so, although the data constantly changes, and is unknowable and unpredictable except in markets.

The assumptions made by the NHS, however, announce and encapsulate our expectations about the roles we each assume and expect. They establish our care conventions, our routines, and what patients expect from the services, from the state, and from themselves. They set the terms of experience in daily practice. They set expectations for the individual managed by the state as a 'patient' who is being 'given' 'care' by the state. Each of these words, with Powell's warning in mind, needs to be watched with scrutiny and scepticism. The contrast is with a person taking self-responsibility. That is, guided by a moral compass, a person with a specific character. This envisages each of us as a moral being valued for his or her own sake, not merely as the subject of an 'outcome', even one we 'help set'. For we are not merely to be envisaged as the recipients of effectiveness, appropriateness, cost-efficiency, technical efficiency, bench-marked services and improved clinical governance.

These are not only issues for the silence of a library. They affect every patient and potential patient. They have, to borrow words from E.L. Doctorow's novel *The Waterworks*, a 'hard, woodpecking quality'.[6] They will not go away. Thus, we need more alertness, suspicion, and clarity about these concepts and labels, and about the essence of the problems—for a start, concerning the words 'rationing' and 'priority setting'. The word 'prioritisation' is a box within a box. For rationing and prioritisation are not the same thing, although the words are often used interchangeably. This is far from being just a quibble. If we are to understand the nature of rationing in a public (i.e., 'political') sector monopoly it is important to see the statue in the marble. In fact, 'rationing' is what government does when it decides on the level of budgets for the NHS. 'Priority setting' is what happens within a *rationed* budget once the totality of that budget is set. The one follows the other.

Politicians and managers dislike the pejorative tone of the word rationing. They prefer the seemingly softer and more purposive ('fairer') words 'priority setting'. This phrase enables them too readily to accept the 'realities' of rationing in a 'fixed' NHS budget. They can say: 'Sorry, but this is a balancing act, and there are technical difficulties about making adequate arrangements'. 'Prioritisation' is a shield, not a searchlight. It avoids the real challenges. Notably, who decides who decides. How, too, professional roles will change.

# 5

# Deficits and Denials:
# The Daily Realities Of Rationing

Meanwhile, we are daily reminded of the realities of rationing in the NHS—notably by waiting lists, by local variation in access to services, and by the displacement of the interests of one group of patients by another group. The levels of service and of performance impose unnecessary suffering. The NHS inexpertly allocates resources, for it marginalises the expertise of the individual actually living the life and it restricts possible funding.

There is much arbitrary and inconsistent decision-making in managing scarcity. Value judgements are made in the eternal decision-making triangle of patient, doctor and payer. These are judgements made case by case, and often between individuals competing for similar (and insufficient) resources. Which patients are the more deserving, who is to decide, how, and on what basis? These choices come up every day in decisions concerning capacity to benefit from treatment. They influence, and are influenced by, decisions on how to spend limited money between different patients. They are pivotal in allocative capital planning, preventive care, screening and early detection. They are a cause of great anxiety, for example amongst cancer patients, whose incidence is soaring in rapidly ageing populations.

The opinions of professionals are perhaps the most influential contribution to making priority decisions between patients within a speciality, especially since broad 'purchasing' decisions do not give guidance on decisions at the level of the individual patient facing the professional at the desk or on the operating table. The potential for diverse practice, not necessarily justified by capacity to benefit—for example, in the resort to dilatation and curetage (D&C) for heavy menstrual bleeding (menorrhagia) which is practised routinely in some regions, but hardly at all in others—is considerable. It is difficult if not impossible for the patient in advance to know how they will be judged ('assessed'), and whether or not they will receive optimal treatment.

The deficits are several, and severe. Service levels are inadequate, as a series of reports from voluntary organisations, from the Health Service Ombudsman, and from the government's own Audit Commission indicate. The NHS does not always perform as it should, medically as well as managerially.

As John Willman recently commented: 'An honest observer would have to admit that the NHS has fallen behind the health services of other countries in terms of the treatment it offers and the quality of its service'. And: 'the NHS falls far short in the quality of its services in comparison with what people would expect in almost any other walk of life'. He adds: 'It is hard to imagine any sphere of commercial life where the preferences of the individual user are given so little weight. The free market may be distorted by monopoly, the manipulation of consumers and shady business practices. But one thing is clear: a consumer with money to spend is treated as the centre of attention and offered the chance to make choices—however partial—in a way that is quite alien to the NHS'.[1]

Look at the deficits we can easily see around us in primary practice, in clinics and hospitals, in mental health care and community services. These all arise as a consequence of policy made to meet financial targets, and from inevitable failings in management in a public-sector monopoly. They concern many capacity issues which question whether there has been the appropriate rate of investment in such things as advanced capital goods, R&D, market development, and skills training. Without high rates of investment in capital per worker and in training and development many deficits and denials arise. Unfortunately, there has been no alignment between market valuation and performance, and a commitment to visionary 'values' has not been able to measure necessary investment. Thus, deficits and attitudes have arisen as the consequence of political decision-making about personal health care. These serious deficits embrace shortages of modern drugs, poor cancer care, unfunded chronic care. There are low salaries—set collectively, rather than individually in response to supply and demand. There is low morale, serious skill and manpower shortages and a need for pay and job reform. There is closed entry to professions, as part of the political arrangements made in the 1940s. There are reduced bed numbers, limited information, lack of time, insufficient incentives, service exclusions. We have noted the plight of the disadvantaged poor.

There are many poor hospital environments. Facilities tend to be elderly, with much out-dated equipment, and a multi-million pound backlog of building maintenance. Ivan Ellul, Deputy Head of the Primary Care General Medical Branch of the NHS Executive, recently stated that: 'In some inner cities, as many as 40 or 50 per cent of practice premises don't even meet the standards set some 30 years ago'.[2]

Mentalities and imaginations, too, are restricted to the 'politically possible'. This idea itself is playing a large part in increasing the stresses within the NHS, for it marginalises the role that leadership can play. Yet political reality changes, and can be changed. It is not a constant. Nor is it necessarily predictable. What is practicable often changes swiftly. Leadership counts. It can help reveal the potential of individuals flourishing independently. Present and temporary 'realities', as Hayek noted, can alter rapidly and should not be allowed to restrict thinking. The word 'impossible' does not mean that something cannot be done, merely that it has not happened yet. Enoch Powell famously articulated this:

> Too often today people are ready to tell us: 'This is not possible, that is not possible'. I say: whatever the true interest of our country calls for is always possible. We have nothing to fear but our own doubts.[3]

The following are amongst the most visible daily deficits—none of which can be laid at the feet of market forces, all of which involve injustice. These and other deficits are taken for granted in a public-sector monopoly.

### i) Medical Manpower and Patient's Hopes of Survival —Exemplified Especially in Unsatisfactory Cancer Care

One of the most significant deficits is medical manpower. There is a serious shortage of clinical specialists—for example in cancer care—and of consultants in anaesthetics, paediatrics and psychiatry. The NHS has not trained enough doctors, or retained enough of those who have qualified. Professional control over entry, mis-estimates of future demand, and low salaries in a rationed system are amongst the explanations. The institutions of medicine, particularly in hospitals—notably the moral damage done to doctors-in-training, and the socialisation of juniors by seniors in hospitals—damage the capacity of doctors to 'see' patients as individuals. This has been noted by researchers, and identified as a major deterrent to many from serving once trained.[4] Nearly 40 per cent of UK medical students decide eventually not to work in the NHS. These problems are clear in one of the most important areas of continuing difficulty—cancer care. The UK is already significantly short of cancer specialists. Yet by 2020 it is predicted that one in two people will develop the disease compared with one in three today.[5]

In the UK there are approximately only 340 medical oncologists, or cancer specialists. Large numbers of cancer patients are treated by general surgeons who do not necessarily see a condition frequently. In the USA, which is commonly assumed to be a less successful model of health care, there are 20,000 oncologists for a population only five times greater than the UK. A British clinical oncologist has an average 560 new patients a year, whereas in Norway the figure is 75, in Germany 140, in France 200.[6]

Not all scarce specialist time is well used. Much senior doctor time can be taken up disputing decisions concerning rationing in individual cases, and pressing the case for an individual to be treated. Health authorities can refuse to consider cases on an individual patient basis. Professor Karol Sikora, the leading oncologist, argues in this book that the rationing of cancer care could be ended by implementing a new structure to provide services in which about 30 expert cancer centres in teaching hospitals and research centres would each link up with ten to twelve cancer units in nearby general hospitals. An investment of a relatively small sum—£100 million—is estimated as needed to dramatically improve the structure of services.

British results are comparatively poor and appreciably poorer in many treatment areas than those of comparable countries.

Although survival rates in England and Wales for cancer patients have improved in the past 20 years, ours are still amongst the worst in the West. For example, the UK still has one of the highest mortality rates for cervical cancer in the developed world: some 1,300 women die from the disease every year. A recent survey found that 48 of 60 health authorities questioned were not committed to providing the combination treatment for ovarian cancer recommended by the Joint Council of Clinical Oncology, and endorsed by the Department of Health's own standing medical advisory committee.[7]

Many specialist units seem to be in crisis, for example in breast cancer where British survival rates are very poor. These units are reported to be experiencing low morale and with nearly half of consultant radiologists looking for another job. Recruitment shortages threaten closure for the national screening programme in some areas, too, according to another recent report.

There is strong evidence that a patient's chances of survival vary depending on where they live, or by whom they are treated. The Thames Cancer Registry shows significant diversity between different boroughs for the five-year survival rates for breast-cancer. A man with prostate cancer in Bexley and Greenwich, in South-East London, has a 34 per cent chance of surviving for five years, while someone living in Chelsea and Kensington has a 59.8 per cent chance. The national average is 45.2 per cent. However, the performance of individual doctors remains secret.[8]

Many NHS hospitals do not attain optimal practice: for example, only a third of hospitals provide the single-visit diagnosis, or 'one-stop' breast cancer diagnosis, that the all-party Committee on Breast Cancer said in October 1998 should be available to all women.[9]

It is a general problem that doctor work-loads are more stressful here than in Europe. The Royal College of Nursing recently reported that most nurses think low staffing levels are putting patients at risk. The Secretary of State for Health recently told NHS managers that they will be subject to legal sanction if they fail to provide statutory standards of service.

There are difficulties, too, in the NHS concerning its testing procedures for varying conditions. A recent report by the National

Audit Office found that only half of NHS laboratories were meeting standards. For example, women were referred with abnormalities to colposcopy clinics which achieved 'poor' waiting targets; nearly half of the clinics are not providing women with key information about colposcopy; a third are not providing information about treatment.[10]

The pressures of shortages are alleged to have 'bred callous doctors', a difficulty said to be frequently reported by cancer sufferers. A lack of time to deal sensitively with distress is said to be compounding the problem, according to Professor David Weatherall, Regius Professor of Medicine at Oxford University. The pressures of over-work and staff shortages have fatal consequences in other clinical areas. A review of childbirth deaths by doctors and midwives recently showed that hundreds of babies are dying every year because of blunders by over-worked and under-trained hospital staff.[11]

There are difficulties at every turn. GPs were recently reported by the Health Service Ombudsman to be too quick to bar patients who complain. The Institute of Health Service Management was recently told that it was not uncommon to find more than half of all patients notes containing errors—seven per cent listing the wrong intended procedure. These are facts. The National Confidential Enquiry Into Perioperative Deaths has reported, in a series of reports since 1987, the reluctance of doctors to participate in audit, inadequate supervision of junior doctors and anaesthetists, and unacceptable variations in work.[12]

There is a genuine question as to whether and how *spare* capacity is possible and affordable in health care, as in other markets. However, no-one should have to be satisfied with an unsatisfactory doctor who is not otherwise in demand, whose services many would not consume at any price. In the USA and Europe there is spare capacity without a decline in standards.

Meanwhile, the pay award for nurses and doctors announced by the NHS in January 1999 will impact on the development of core services for cancer and mental health, as the increase cannot be met from this year's spending increase, according to professional bodies.[13]

## ii) No Guarantee Or Right To Service

There are no guarantees that the individual can obtain a service from the welfare state. The NHS gives no guarantees or right to treatment, despite its emphasis on 'fairness' and access. A right of access to a waiting-list (if a GP and a consultant agree—the individual cannot go directly to a specialist, unlike in Europe) is not the same as a right to treatment. The difference between a service being legally and actually available often hurts.

For the individual seeking an intimate service, the key is not the epic of what is promised. It is what the individual can actually get when they want it, or when their medical adviser says they should get a service. A political promise is insufficient if there is no binding legal entitlement guaranteeing that a service will be provided, if there is no financial leverage to command provision, and if there is no competitive alternative.

## iii) Nursing And Other Staff Shortages

In September 1998 there were estimated to be 8,000 nursing vacancies. The NHS Trust Confederation estimated that 78 per cent of hospitals have serious difficulties recruiting nurses and other health professionals. Some 40 per cent of nurses leave the profession on qualification. In 1997 2,700 NHS staff nurses left. One in five nurses takes a second job to supplement income. Senior doctors estimate that between one-fifth and 40 per cent of UK medical students decide eventually not to work in the NHS. There are over 1,000 unfilled GP posts, and surgeries are often vastly over-crowded. A shortage of midwives was recently reported as being responsible for the inability to provide expectant mothers with a pain-killing epidural on demand and for the early discharge of new mothers. In addition, there are estimated to be 1,000 unfilled physiotherapy posts and 1,000 midwifery vacancies in the NHS.

There are continuing and apparently endemic problems of recruitment and retention of all staff. Salaries, and professional numbers, are each depressed in the UK. Administrative salaries, too, lag behind comparable levels overseas. Recruitment and training costs are higher than necessary; sickness rates exceed normal industrial rates. Morale is poor, frustration high—in part because staff can see the gap between what they can do and what could be done if funding were available for optimal services. Staff turnover is high, and the built environment—despite some attractive modern hospitals—is often unpleasant, cheap but not cheerful. Costs, too, vary by a factor of six, according to the government's own National Schedule of Reference Costs.[14]

### iv) Clinical Quality And Practice

There has been a series of very serious difficulties with the performance of clinicians, for example, the tragedy revealed only very recently at Bristol Royal Infirmary involving the deaths of 29 babies in the child heart unit. On this case a writer in *The Guardian* recently commented (printing two articles titled 'Doctors ignored their critics' and 'Small children kept dying, but the doctors ignored their critics'):

> With only 10 similar units across the country, one might have thought that reported death rates that were double those of the others over seven years would have attracted attention. As it was, the scandal only came to light when an anaesthetist blew the whistle, making himself deeply unpopular.[15]

In addition, the chief executive of the Trust was a doctor. This suggests that over-reliance on self-regulation by professionals has been allowed by governments who know they cannot fully fund demand and who thus rely on professionals to manage the tensions. This seems to have had serious consequences in unexpected variations in clinical practice and in the quality of care.

Professor Rudolf Klein has argued, in reviewing the Bristol events, that there have been few accepted standards or benchmarks against which performance could be judged, either by doctors or by others. There has been an unwillingness to expose inadequacies; there has been institutional complicity and the urge to protect colleagues. There has been, too, what Klein has called 'institutional imperialism', as well as the passivity of the Department of Health, regional authorities and the Royal Colleges in the face of evidence concerning inadequacies. There are challenges which require fundamental changes, as the President of the General Medical Council Sir Donald Irvine recognised when summarising the wider issues raised by the Bristol case. These include the necessity to change attitudes within the Royal Colleges, the medical schools, the NHS Trusts and in the minds of individual doctors. Crucially, the need for a critical awareness of individual performance and the consequent risks to patients has been underlined.

The inquiry, however, was thought 'too narrow in its scope and too lenient in its judgement'. Klein says that 'It was not just three doctors who were on trial before the GMC. It was, in effect, an institution: The Bristol Royal Infirmary'. In fact, the institution on trial was wider than that. It was the long-established relationship between government, professions and managers, which had excluded the patient as the first point of reference but which was still toothless in being able to influence standards effectively. On trial was the existing machinery of professional self-regulation, the necessary protection of the public, and the relationship between that machinery and government assertions concerning quality in 'the best health service in the world'. As Klein says, 'there remains a widespread sense of public frustration left by the Bristol case—the sense that it had raised more questions than it had answered about the delivery of safe medical care'.

There are a number of factors, generally falling under the heading of 'the institutions of medical practice' which have become more evident. Notably, the fact that hospital trust chief executives and boards have been accountable for everything that happens in their hospitals, except the thing which matters the most to patients, which is the quality of the medical care they receive. *The King's Fund Review* referred to 'the rather meagre system of accountability that has characterised the NHS for most of its life'. The medical profession—and the chief executives and Boards— have not been either individually or collectively accountable for performance. Only now, after Bristol and after the 50th anniversary celebrations of the NHS, is clinical performance being addressed by a public-sector monopoly.

The governmental role of accreditation, of inspection and enhancement of clinical performance to protect patients is significantly stronger in the United States. There is the wide-spread development and publication of detailed medical care data. The clinical competence of surgical practitioners is more openly addressed. There is better record-keeping and documentation. This alternative to self-regulation impacts on training, career development, reward, and quality. The American system goes significantly beyond the Commission for Health Improvement (CHIMP) and National Institute for Clinical Excellence (NICE) (which is concerned with clinical excellence, not with cost-effectiveness). Malpractice reform will not by itself produce the dramatic changes required in health care. Yet British responses are embedded in self-regulation.[16] The situation is clearly different with regard to quality, regulation and accountability in the USA, precisely because there is more individual influence over the levels of funding. Purchasing of care is done on behalf of individuals by health plans which specify what they want from professionals and what they will provide for subscribers.

Steven Henning Sieverts argues, too, that the federal US government's National Practitioner Data Bank offers the potential for analysis and empowered choice at many new levels. But there is no equivalent in the UK enabling analysis and comparison of doctors with their peers, hospitals with each other, and the re-assurance that we are being served by those who reach the highest standards. The NHS system of financing is one of the denials of this potential. For it decides not only how much can be spent but denies the individual the right to move 'his/her' fund or to add to it for preferred services.[17]

### v) Post-code Rationing

There is no national uniformity of practice and purchasing of care. This may be actually both undesirable and impossible to achieve. However, it is noticeable, by contrast with the hopes of many planners, that this varies widely, unpredictably and surprisingly. There is the notorious rationing by post-code. There is, too, the recent admission (by a member of the NHS Executive) that there is 'a large element of "pot luck" in the standard of primary care'. Yet the NHS depends on primary care for 80 per cent of all trcatments, and for successful referral to specialists, in time and to the right person. In addition, patients have been urged to move house if they want treatment denied by their local health authority.[18]

Much consumption of health services depends on the referral behaviour and preference of GPs and consultants. Practice patterns vary to a surprising extent, in part because the knowledge base in many treatment areas in uncertain. Even when it is analysed, many doctors prefer older approaches.

### vi) Secrecy And Poor Information

One attribute of scarcity is that it is very difficult for patients to discover basic facts. Who are the specialists? Where are the specialist centres located? Information given to patients is often 'seriously misleading', out-of-date and inaccurate, according to a recent King's Fund assessment.[19] There are strong lobbies which keep issues and information suppressed.

There are many issues here concerning open information about public services. Whose information is it? Who designed it, and for which purposes? Who is to determine what is and is not to be open? How can information be transformed into knowledge, and then into individual leverage, to make differences between people count? If patients do get information, can it make a difference? For this to be true, services must be responsive, legal services must be actually available, and able to be commanded by the consumer. The NHS does not ensure that information is available, nor that it means something for the consumer. One consequence is that the modernisation of the NHS, with the fullest successful development of community medicine, is greatly hindered. Informed consumers, too, may consume less.

### vii)  Often No Choice of GP, And No Guidance on How To Join a Practice

The denial of clear information begins with the patient joining a GP practice, where more than 80 per cent of present services are rendered. There is no guidance on selecting a GP, nor on the reasons for varying practice styles and their possible consequences. However, a recent study by the Medical Defence Union showed that over half of successful claims, amounting to almost £8 million, against family doctors arose because they delayed diagnosing the patient's condition. There is often no genuine choice in selecting a GP. Many GPs tell potential patients they are not adding to their list; women cannot be guaranteed to have a female doctor if they prefer this; there are fewer choices in rural areas; the proposed large primary care groups will lead to primary care trusts with population-catchments of 100-400,000, greatly limiting choice and exit. The distribution of GPs per head of population is, too, a cause of inequity, as is the quality of GP services in poorer areas. The lack of price or incentive to responsibility is also damaging. One GP wrote recently: 'In my practice patients did not attend more than 1,400 booked appointments last year. If I could charge them for failing to attend, this might not happen'.[20] Poor NHS communications are often at fault, too.

### viii) The Denial of Modern Drugs

These denials dramatise rationing. For example, a modern drug like Interferon-beta (which can slow the progression of multiple sclerosis) is entirely denied to many patients. This drug appears to delay the progress of one form of the illness, cuts the number of relapses and improves symptoms. It can also increase the length of time before a sufferer goes into sustained decline. However, campaign groups estimate that only 15 per cent of those who could benefit from it are receiving it. Some half of the 85,000 - 100,000 suffering from MS in Britain have the 'relapse-remitting' form. In terms of the NHS concern with 'efficacy', this drug is effective in producing good patient benefit for significant numbers even if it is expensive in absolute terms. However, it is made available to only 1,100 of the 10,000 sufferers in Britain who are judged suitable for treatment with the drug. Patients themselves have no opportunity for cost-conscious life-chance choice. There are Department of Health limits on its availability 'free' on the NHS. The Department has doubts about its effectiveness —although these have been discounted in recent studies in the *Lancet*—and worries about its cost.[21] One estimate suggests that if 16,000 people took the drug this could cost the NHS £152 million. Many would like the state to pay, or to be able to pay for themselves. In January 1999 the British Medicine Control Agency was reported as set to approve a new licence for beta interferon 1b, for which up to 30,000 more MS sufferers would be eligible for treatment. However, many health authorities have indicated they will not pay for it. Similar problems arise with the uneven delivery of combination therapy for AIDS, the prescription of Aricept for Alzheimer's and Metastvan for prostate cancer patients, all of which are unevenly purchased by different and adjacent health authorities.[22]

There is a common assumption in the NHS that patients would not pay for drugs if they could. This idea is discounted by the reports of cancer patients willing to pay. When patients have found themselves denied a service there is evidence that some at least would wish to make additional payments. Professor Karol Sikora says that terminally ill cancer patients—suffering from cancer of the colon, breast, ovaries or lungs—are increasingly paying for drugs to prolong their lives. Prostate cancer patients can be helped with hormonal drugs which provide extra months of 'quality life', but these are not always funded. Here, there is no question of patients not minding missing what they have never had. They are finding out what might help them; they are aware of the restraints imposed by the NHS; they have shown themselves willing to pay for extra drugs if they can do so.[23]

This potential, too, has been dramatically highlighted by the inadvertent innovation of Viagra, a drug intended for angina treatment but embraced instead for the treatment of impotency. The drug has again under-scored that much health-care is a matter of lifestyle choice, not of emergency care. It is thus eminently suited to individual choice and empowered preference.

L'affaire-Viagra shows that governments have discarded and suppressed mechanisms by which individuals can decide their own priorities in selecting a health plan or a preferred therapy, thus engaging in the key adult activity of learning to choose.

Those who suggest that people are unwilling to pay often consider that people should not be allowed to pay, even if they can do so and wish to do so. The argument is one of equity. However, it clearly limits the freedom of some on the ostensible basis of enlarging (or not diminishing) the freedom of others. The reality is that people who would prefer to buy drugs instead of beer, a new car, a holiday, a larger house, are unable to make this cost-conscious choice.

This is a question that concerns not only 'lifestyle' drugs such as Viagra. It concerns sufferers from clinical conditions for which a drug alleviation is legal but rationed. For example, the drug Aricept (for treating Alzheimer's disease) may only be prescribed by hospital consultants. GPs, too, knowing that money is limited, may not refer patients with costly conditions. Rationing and a 'free' health service are intrinsically intertwined. Our eligibility for care is decided by others on our behalf, in part on cost grounds but also—notably in renal care—on grounds of age and geography, and, for some conditions, even on grounds of gender. Similarly, too, the Secretary of State for Health decided in January 1999 that the principle of universality should be again breached for patients wishing to receive Viagra, for he made Viagra a Schedule 11 drug, which made it available for only some patients, thus making a choice between categories of patients. Here, the objective was to control costs. In addition, he suggested that those who still wanted the treatment should get it, if they wished to pay for it, by asking for a private prescription.[24] The present system does not take account of individual demand; it discourages both self-responsibility and a mutual concern for others.

### ix) Renal Care: An Example Of Capacity To Benefit Denied

The NHS denies many patients services from which they have the capacity to benefit. A very explicit example is renal care: the rationing or non-provision of services which can save the lives of those with chronic kidney failure is significant. Britain treats significantly fewer patients with renal failure than most European countries. It ranks twenty-first in Europe in the numbers of new patients accepted for treatment each year, and the position is becoming worse according to the European Dialysis and Transplant Association. Willman notes: 'Only Bulgaria treats fewer patients per head of population per year'.[25] The NHS is also reducing the quality of its service for those to whom it does offer treatment: for example, many are now offered haemodialysis twice a week instead of three times. Home dialysis is greatly restricted, as are other preferred modern facilities. Many patients are denied the gains of modern innovation: for example, access to the most modern 'cocktail' of immuno-suppressant drugs in transplant on grounds of cost. This frustrates professional and patient alike. The NHS also restricts access to renal care on the basis of age and geography, which reflects directly an inadequate financial base. In addition, there are wide variations in achieving national clinical targets. Transplant surgery itself is on 'a knife edge' in British hospitals because of a shortage of donors and medical specialists, according to the Royal College of Surgeons. Some 5,300 people are currently waiting for transplants, and about 10 per cent will die or become too ill before a suitable organ becomes available.[26]

In the USA, as Sieverts has recently stressed, renal services are much better, as they are in Europe. In the USA, for example, every person who suffers kidney failure is entitled by law to dialysis services and to transplant services if medically necessary. The bill is paid either by a private insurance plan or by the joint state/federal Medicare programme. There is no such entitlement in the UK. In the USA people in their eighties benefit from dialysis and transplantation and lead useful and fulfilled lives. In the UK they are denied these services, which are strictly rationed. Generally, life threatening conditions are treated in the NHS, but not in this case.[27]

With a low level of total expenditure, the NHS is slower to adopt some major new technologies than other OECD countries. Innovations are necessarily curtailed, withheld, or delayed. The problems of renal care are an example of the fact that in more broadly-based systems of funding there is more dispersal of high and low technology. The treatment of renal illness, lithotripsy (the blasting away of kidney stones) is less frequent here than in many European countries, because Britain has fewer lithotripters. For example, Belgium—a relatively small country—has 800,000 people per machine, whereas Britain has 3.8 million.[28]

The best test of a care system is that people can get services when and how they want them, for example, when they experience kidney failure. In the NHS there is much proven, unmet, unfinanced, unempowered want of treatment. There is unnecessary early death. Services are observably provided more successfully in mixed-finance systems in Europe which combine state, private and voluntary services and funding. Lives unnecessarily lost here are saved in Europe. Patients enjoy improved independent living. In a cash-limited system, by contrast, the rationing of renal care is remorselessly explicit. Cost is an issue for the state, at whatever level of demand. This is so, too, for the individual. But many who would like to meet additional costs, and thus prompt an increased supply of specific and desired services (such as home dialysis), have no mechanism for doing so within the present NHS structure. In renal care—and it is only one example—there is a genuine risk of NHS services being pushed to the lowest safe level in a cash-limited system, whilst also denying service to many people in disapproved categories such as the elderly.

This is a systemic, structural, *imposed* failure which stands alongside the natural constraints of our lives.

### x) Services For Women

There is a significant difficulty for women, who many believe generally receive a poorer service. For example, there is evidence that some male doctors discount the concerns of women which they take more seriously if the patient presenting is a man. One example recently reported concerned the case of a 28-year-old woman who died of cancer two years after being told by a male doctor that she was 'a silly woman who read too many women's magazines and watched too much television'. Her family was awarded damages after her death. This woman could have gone elsewhere if there had been a published patient audit of doctors and if NHS tax-funds were mobile and individual. There are, too, difficulties for women who prefer a woman doctor in primary care consultations. Only some patients can get the choice of a woman doctor. In Berkshire, for example, 80 per cent (only) of practices offer that choice; in Rotherham, only 30 per cent do so.[29]

### xi) Complaints

John Willman, in his analysis of opinion, commented: 'whatever people say about the NHS being the best in the world, there is great dissatisfaction with it'.[30]

Public dissatisfaction is rising. In the period April - September 1998 the Parliamentary Health Ombudsman received a record number of complaints.[31] They are some measure—in the absence of price and cost-conscious choice—of the call for reform. They are, too, some measure of the gap between NHS theory and practice. They indicate what ordinary people 'know' but find it difficult to articulate or to influence, but which—once expressed—we see that we 'knew'. They help us glimpse an alternative account of NHS experience to the published version of 'best in the world'. They are the unheard voices of those who, when they complain, often receive letters from the NHS explaining why things must be the way that they are. There is a suspicion that we are seeing here not a disregarded minority, but a disregarded majority. The complaints suggest that the experience of what it is like to be treated in the NHS is often different from the official narrative. Levels of dissatisfaction have doubled in recent years, according to the British Social Attitudes Survey. [32]

The level of complaints is one of the few measures of public indignation at poor services, but it has no leveraged outlet which can re-assert the sovereignty of the consumer. Voice, vote and money are disconnected.

The National Consumer Council found, too, that many patients did not complain about NHS treatment and experiences because they found the prospect too daunting. Three out of four who complained to their GPs received no response. Two out of three who complained to hospitals were also ignored.

GPs are said to drop one in ten patients because they ask too many questions about medical treatment, according to a recent report. Mentally ill patients, too, are reported to be given only basic care.[33]

## xii)  Privacy And Dignity

Such basics as patient dignity and privacy are not a high priority for investment. In the UK—and this despite vibrant patient campaigning—mixed wards persist. Yet, overseas, one-bedded rooms are common. In the USA, the government's own Medicare programme (covering the poor) has entitled its beneficiaries to a two-bedded room *for more than thirty years*. Willman comments:

Few would tolerate these conditions on holiday or on a business trip when they had paid for the accommodation. Imagine your reaction if your package holiday turned out to involve sharing a mixed ward dormitory. Or if the staff in the hotel were so stressed and overworked that you could not get the service you were entitled to. Yet these conditions are accepted as normal when we undergo the far more stressful experience of hospital treatment.[34]

Help the Aged recently launched the 'Dignity on the Ward' campaign, following a shock survey released in 1997 which revealed grave concerns about the care of older people in NHS hospitals, notably on attitudes to those who are captive consumers. Attitudes, care issues, relationships with front-line staff, delays in admission, the poor environment, equipment shortages, staff shortages, food and drink, privacy and dignity, communications, the boundaries of care and discharge procedures were all cause for great concern. This prompted the Secretary of State for Health to write to all hospital chief executives again to insist on the necessity to 'ensure that the basics—such as clean dry sheets and proper standards and provision of food and drink—are available to all patients'.[35]

### xiii) The Plight of The Poor

The NHS structure has proved to be particularly disadvantageous for those originally expected to gain the most. For the poor still do least well in terms of morbidity and mortality. They lack social command and cultural power in networks. And they are cut off from the one thing which is more commanding than cultural power, which is money.

The government's own *Independent Enquiry into Inequalities in Health* led by Sir Donald Acheson recently stressed that the individual matters.[36] However, it stands rooted in the past, on the platform of discredited ideas. First, it approached the individual in the NHS collectivist spirit of someone to be acted upon, to be supervised and improved. Second, it blamed income inequality, rather than *absolute* poverty (thus suggesting that good health is a zero-sum game) for inequalities in health. Third, it called for a further collectivised tilt of resources towards the 'poor', but with no individual leverage. That is, more of the same. Yet low income groups have done least well in terms of morbidity and mortality during half a century of public-sector monopoly in the NHS. Thus, Acheson proposed more social-engineering: much improved benefits, better housing, more jobs, improved pre-school education and policies to reduce the income gap between rich and poor. And thus, to provide the poor with a greater share of rationed goods.

Certainly, improved public health programmes would have *some* impact on health status, although many diseases are diseases of affluence not poverty (heart disease, notably). However, a further dose of well-meaning, collectivised social engineering would not in itself provide personal incentives for changes in behaviour and responsibility (for one's self, for one's family, for one's neighbours). Nor would such social engineering in itself do anything to bring people more effectively into the market-place for better health care—for example by tax transfers, price-signals, and by discouraging those dependencies and family failures influenced by many factors other than income.

The welfarist alternative has failed those with low incomes and those without persuasive 'class' power. Acheson's route is not the best hope, as has been shown by the quality and diversity of life-choices and goods gained by the general population in competitive markets. Here, dissatisfied consumers can reject poor service.[37]

### xiv) *Too Little Audit And Analysis Of What Matters To Patients*

There is little understanding within the NHS or in government of how well what really counts is actually being done. Some 80 per cent of all interventions occur in primary care. Yet there is little analysis of GP referral decisions, of how well GPs succeed comparatively in spotting treatable disease, of how well they do in getting appropriate patients to an appropriate specialist, swiftly and first time. We know little of how effective treatments have been, because the NHS does not systematically track patients over time on a sample basis and report back. Doctors, too, are not encouraged to say 'I don't know', to confess uncertainty, to share uncertainty with patients and to explore the alternatives. Here, patients and professionals share the blame. Thus, doctors can and do disregard an important requirement, expressed by a general practitioner: 'Signs and symptoms, even investigations, must not be squeezed into an unpromising diagnosis'. This is both a problem of medical mystique, and of patient expectations divorced from self-responsibility.[38]

Clinical Audit, too, surprisingly, has been optional for doctors, and many have not co-operated. There has been no penalty for refusal. Local NHS trust and health authority chief executives have not managed clinical performance, nor analysed it systematically. Boards have not addressed it. The NHS is still searching, too, for effective ways to stop ineffective care and to spread best practice.[39]

There is little consistent and systematic analysis of the effectiveness, appropriateness, cost-efficiency, and technical efficiency of accident and emergency (A&E) work. Yet it is here that half of all NHS activity occurs. For example, we do not know how comparatively efficient was initial assessment of patients in A&E. Nor how what was done compared with what was initially thought necessary. Nor what results are like. We know little about cost-effectiveness or outcomes. What we do know, from the Audit Commission studies of such issues as how promptly people are treated, indicates the failure of the NHS to organise itself to put the patient first. The Audit Commission and the national media have highlighted how poorly managed are many accident and emergency departments. The elderly, research suggests, are particularly poorly served. In December 1998 a woman of 82 needed 30 stitches after falling from a trolley as she lay unattended in a hospital emergency unit. An 89-year-old man was left on a hospital trolley for 18 hours before being sent home because a bed could not be found for him. In January 1999 the Association of Community Health Councils published a new nationwide survey which showed what nursing and health care workers described as 'inhuman' and 'unacceptable' waiting times in A&E departments. One 84-year-old man had waited on a trolley nearly 29 hours for a bed.[40] Willman commented on the earlier analysis by the Audit Commission:

> The overwhelming message from the Commission's analysis is that hospitals have simply not geared themselves up to admit emergency patients in an acceptable manner—one of the most basic steps in the treatment of patients.[41]

# 6

# A Perspective On Deficits

As we have seen, a key issue is that individuals have no say in the spending of 'their' money, therefore individual patients have no power to encourage the local provider to furnish a service. Nor are they entitled to go elsewhere to get it and to take the money with them. Patient 'demand' cannot be individually expressed. Nor is it empowered in a way which encourages doctors and hospitals (or potential new providers) to respond to cash flow (or cash ebb) provided by patient demand or its withdrawal. As Sieverts (who appears critical of right-wing thinkers) says of the US position:

> After all, if additional beds and nurses, or the magnetic resonance imager or the neonatal intensive care unit is what patients need [by which, in this context, he means 'want'], and providers are assured they will be reimbursed for providing them, little will dampen their growth. The combining of collective entitlement with collective payment for services feeds the resource expansion, for better or worse.[1]

Sieverts offers an important view of the lie of the land, as an 'insider/outsider':

> For the 80 per cent-plus of the American people who enrol in private or public medical insurance programmes, queues for even the most specialised service are hard to find. Hospitals by and large don't have waiting lists. If a particular specialist doctor's practice is completely full, he or she is likely to engage a partner to handle the additional demand...This isn't true in many rural areas, of course, or in some inner city slums, but it is a valid generalisation about the parts of America where most people live.[2]

It is evident that such a structure underpins higher levels of spending in most comparable European countries, as well as in North America and Australia. Elsewhere, there are more beds, more doctors, more nurses, more support services and ambulatory care facilities for each 1,000 of population. The historian Harold Perkin has studied the rise of modern professional society, and the relationship between professionals and government, which favours the interests of both.[3] There is a limited number of doctors because of the arrangements made to persuade professionals to join the NHS in 1948.[4] There are no market mechanisms (except in the small private sector) which enable the consumer to command the doctor, and to encourage more supply. Britain, as a consequence, has a poor ratio of doctors to patients.

The USA, despite its difficulties in some well-recognised respects, has no waiting lists for medical or surgical services, even among low-income people covered by the state. This is so even for the uninsured, who are covered by Medicaid. The system depends on open information for the consumer to consider, and the insuring organisation—whether health maintenance organisation (HMO) or government—responding with service. In the NHS, however, information itself is rationed. Thus, calls for increases in taxation to pay for the NHS announce the problem but not the solution. For by its finance *regime* the state suppresses the opportunity for people to pay more for their care if they wish. And this despite the fact that medicine is much more often a consumer good than a crisis buy.

There are many consequences, which in the planning structures should be thought of as deliberate and intended consequences of a state-financed, state-provided, near-monopoly system of health care. The problems are not fortuitous, nor accidental. They are endemic, systemic, and they are avoidable. But still many refuse to see. As Wyndham remarks: 'There are times when one fails to see why God thought it necessary to devise the ostrich'.[5]

### The Nature Of The Challenge and How The NHS Responds

There are a number of factors which are concurrently hastening the NHS to crisis. These reveal the twin difficulties of rationing from a narrow financial base, and without individual cost-conscious awareness and responsibility. Internal and external pressures are changing the threshold in multiple respects between the patient and care. Many of these influences act independently of government policy. They increase unpriced demand for services by voters, by potential patients, by GPs, by hospital specialists.

Newly available diagnostic techniques, treatments and technologies generate new expectations for conditions previously untreatable or untreated. They reveal possibilities previously unthought of, and difficult to fund. There are many new things we didn't know we wanted, which we couldn't get, which we now say we cannot do without, but whose relative costs and benefits are unknown to us. However, increasingly the state (or tax-payer) cannot or will not pay.

There is a formidable list of pressures requiring attention: the increase in life-expectancy and the size of the elderly cohort; increased morbidity; success in reducing mortality; increased demand from a larger cohort of the elderly (the system being punished for its successes); increased scope for treating elderly people. Examples are in eye care (the queue for eye-surgery, mainly cataract removal for the elderly, has risen by 140 per cent in the past ten years) and in renal care/transplants. There are significant improvements in anaesthetic techniques, and greater safety for the elderly. There are opportunities for therapies to be offered to more people, including those for whom earlier therapies were unsafe; developments in new drugs (which may increase or reduce the demand for elective surgery); developments in other medical technologies and newly available therapies; improved diagnostic intelligence; changes in social attitudes which prompt the expectation of treatments; and greater discrimination between providers and between specialists. There is, too, the politicised pressure from the public health lobby to explore, identify, articulate and seek to meet 'unmet need' (which, as I analyse below, is linked to a welfarist mentality and to the function of the NHS as a political equaliser).

The genomic revolution will be bigger than all the other pressures taken together. The political union of Europe may, too, eventually imply the harmonisation of very diverse health care systems.

Government is responding to these pressures:

- by allocating more tax-funds to the NHS
- by trying to improve its consultative techniques, to justify 'prioritisation'

- by constructing a more explicit and firmer basis for rationing decisions, with new emphasis on clinical effectiveness (or evidence-based care)

However, there are several important factors which will continue to complicate the picture.

First, as I have suggested, the NHS has no transparent, rational, and valid method by which it can it sort out who should get what, where and when. It cannot discover who values what, who would pay for what, who would prefer one thing rather than another, what trade-offs individuals would make. It is difficult to compare the benefits from different treatments for different people, cost-effectively and in terms of different outcomes. How are these judgements to be made? Only individuals can truly make these judgements for themselves, but they have no power by which to do so. The conundrum remains: if government, professional, manager and patient have different views, whose is to predominate? Whose preference should be maximised, and how?

Second, the NHS has no mechanisms to gauge relative benefit between individuals and treatments. For judging effectiveness is a subjective process as much as it is a matter of objective judgement and measurement. People are guided by beliefs, choices, sentiments or habits. It is not always 'obvious' that the provider is the 'expert'. Nor that the provider has no economic interest. It is, indeed, more helpful to think of individual patients as the experts on themselves, on their condition, and on their preferred outcome. Providers may have available more technical 'knowledge' and information. But this is one only of the factors relevant to a decision by an individual.

Third, much that is attempted clinically is not of proven value. And even when there is agreement within the professions and with government on 'appropriate treatments', the NHS finds it difficult to achieve changes in practice.

The difficulties become clear when rationers make judgements about the quality of the processes, the practitioner and the alternatives.

Providers, too, are economic actors in the relationship. For in policy and in the offer of choices, the 'proxy agents' (health authority, GP, specialist) occupy several simultaneous and contradictory roles: as advocate, as planner, as marketer, as rationer.

The state is seeking to square the pressures on government by a large programme of tightening up. Here it has been helped by recent clinical events. These revelations (that doctors are not all the same; that practice varies startlingly; that competence cannot be taken for granted; that self-regulation fails the consumer) have helped shift the initiative away from professionals. Government is high-lighting the concepts of effectiveness, appropriateness, cost-efficiency, technical efficiency, more bench-marking (together with budgetary controls) and improved clinical governance (with its implicit challenges to self-regulation, to 'guild science' and mystery). This is the renewed armoury, the political tactics, of priority setting. It seeks to improve costs and outcomes, and to offer a rational basis for 'prioritisation'. It does so around the focus of 'quality', which, as we have seen, is not an objective judgement. Effectiveness is not an absolute. The changes proposed, isolated from competitive markets, offer shaky scaffolding. This is due both to economic truths and to fundamental uncertainties about what is meant by effectiveness, of how to calculate and measure it, of how to distribute it between differing patients.

### The World-Wide Web: A New Market-making Mechanism

The present NHS answers to rationing questions thus seem very unstable. They are becoming difficult to defend, as powerful new 'market-making' mechanisms—notably, the world-wide web—change patient assumptions and possibilities, generate advances in information technology, and continue to influence the sources of competitive advantage.

The web personalises the rationing dilemmas. It does so by increasing the information component of health services—by distributing information held by patients and patient groups, and querying deficits. It is identifying high-quality providers with good medical outcomes and lower prices. It is sharing experiences between patients who have to decide about new experiences, and whom to trust. This matters vitally when health care purchases are one-time events, where past personal experiences are not necessarily any guide. The web is offering valuable comparative information based on meaningful medical outcome measures. These are different judgements to the complexity of medicine itself. The web is thus supporting informed requests for treatments. It is posing mature new questions about what a patient needs to know to get the service, to make a choice, to achieve the desired outcome. The right outcomes are under scrutiny: what are the short- and long-term outcomes of treatment for particular diseases by specific providers, taking into account the general health of the individual? The web is showing that health care is not a monolithic service. It is a myriad of types of services. There are many possible outcomes. There are varied providers. Choice requires information and outcome measures at the level of specific conditions, treatments and providers. The web offers a beginning based on what patients tell one another, to contrast with aggregate comparisons of provider networks.

One key gap is being revealed. This is that being referred to a doctor by itself tells the patient nothing about his or her characteristics, and the likely outcomes in their lives. There is, therefore, pressure to increase (in Michael Porter's terms) the particular data available by which to guide decision making openly. However, the NHS is volume-based and volume-judged. The NHS is not equipped to offer this intensity of information, this particularisation of data on which doctor, which treatment, which side-effect, which outcome. Yet it is in its fifty-first year.

The web is highlighting the importance of differentiation, the key not only to competitiveness but to outcomes. For differences between doctors are seen to matter. There are patient initiatives to distribute this buyer's information, and to increase it.[6]

This is a global discovery process, which creates new demands. It will require doctors to 'embed the information in the product', to use the language of the information technologist: for example, data on alternative outcomes, and, for hospital services, on rates of repair, infection rates, unexpected recall, death, pain management and mobility. The web thus offers the potential for large shifts in the conditions of both demand and supply. It will shift the boundaries between the political power exerted by government over health care provision and the economic power of demand. The web offers new links, and changes in imagination, information and understanding. It re-shapes products themselves, for the entire package of goods and services, information content and value is altered by it. It is transforming the way activities are performed. It is altering the nature of linkages between them. It is re-shaping the way products meet buyers' wishes.

The web is informing and linking patients who are asking the most challenging questions, notably 'why not?' This queries national political processes such as health care rationing. People, too, are discovering that no other country has copied the NHS. It may be the best in the world, from the viewpoint of the Treasury, but many people elsewhere achieve a different level of services—for example, cancer patients and heart/lung-disease patients in the USA. The web makes visible what is considered 'normal' overseas but which is seen as curious in the UK. Notably, people see that services need not necessarily be provided by the state, nor purchased by the state, nor only accessed in facilities owned or managed by the state.

The web is, indeed, doing something to correct the usual medical situation where sellers know more than buyers about the technology of production, the alternatives, and the possible and varying results. The web reveals more of who gets what, where, and with what results, here and overseas. The individual is learning to discriminate risk (and could learn to insure against it rather than surrender it to the political process). People are learning again to exercise their own ingenuity and thoughtfulness, linked to others who help them find out who and what is 'out there'. That is, which choice will work for the individual, in terms of their personal situation and preferred coping strategy. Patients are learning who to trust and who not to trust; many are learning to trust themselves. But individual patients are not yet financially empowered so that consumers can express dissatisfactions and move their business. It is this 'missing link' which should be added to the chain.

These discussions, too, are making more people aware that much medical care concerns lifestyle choices, rather than emergency care or 'welfare' choices.

The web draws attention to the strength, size, and proliferation of patient groups. These do many valuable things. The patient group is valued in offering advice on alternatives. They are changing the balance of information and of mystique. Is it sufficient to empower the patient group? No, it is not. Nor is it satisfactory to envisage the patient group in a political role. We have, indeed, to be cautious of their collaborative 'political' role, seeking accommodations with government. Many take part in rationing consultations, bidding for resources, effectively as a functioning part of government. They are often the source of calls concerning 'under-funding'.[7] Such groups (many very large, and powerful) are closely tied into the 'consultative' political (and honours) process. They embody 'the concept of the consumer as a person to be made over into a basis for political organisation, and even manipulation by the media, by partisan pressure groups, and by other special interest lobbies', in the words of Professor David Marsland. Many are significantly funded by government directly in grant-aid, since government prefers to deal with 'client' groups rather than free individuals. The temptation is to become an advocate of the state. Such bodies can unwittingly harm the patient's interest by hindering the evolution of a market of self- and service-discovery. They often focus on concessions (or 'rents') from government—their 'political representatives'—rather than its replacement with the spontaneous and changeable delivery of personal services by alternative providers. As Arthur Seldon has noted:

> The political process of democracy has impaired the power of the people to learn from experience in protecting themselves from both irregular, unquantifiable uncertainty and recurrable insurance risk. This is the historic failure of democracy: it has prevented or discouraged the people from learning from the discovery process of the market. It has confused the few services that for a time may have to be collectivised in the state from the many which could better have been personalised through the market.[8]

The opportunity is for open government, individual choice, and the moral benefits of the self-owned individual in what David Green has called 'a community without politics'.[9] This requires the move from 'needs' to 'wants'.

# 7

# Moving From 'Needs' To 'Wants'

The NHS eliminated the sovereignty of the consumer in health care. It was intended that it should do so. Shirley Letwin pointed out:

> The NHS was designed to satisfy 'needs' rather than 'wants'. 'Needs' are given by nature, and only experts, doctors and social scientists can know how to satisfy them. Therefore, the patient is to be seen not as a consumer, deciding what he wants, but as a passive recipient of whatever the all-knowing powers on high decide that he ought to have. Therefore consumer sovereignty would defeat the purpose of a national health service ... [the organisation] aimed to treat passive bundles of 'needs', rather than independent consumers with a will to choose what they wanted and a right to complain about how their wants were being satisfied.[1]

## The 'Needs' Model

The NHS is set up on the so-called 'needs' model of health care systems, by contrast with the 'wants', or 'market' model.[2] Each seeks to address the inherent characteristics of health care. Each offers an adaptation to enable governments and individuals to cope. But they are at opposite poles as explanatory models.

In the 'needs' model, 'needs' are 'assessed' by others on behalf of the patient. This 'objective' role in judging necessity and efficacy is given to officials. They struggle to improve their 'knowledge' by consultation, improved information, enhanced understanding. They have the responsibility to control the mix and volume of care. The idea here is that someone can know another person's priorities better than they can know them themselves, and that this is an appropriate basis for deciding who should get what. Academic analysts, with professionals, construct 'measures' of cost-effectiveness which seek to 'efficiently' ration health care 'fairly'. The endeavour then becomes a problem of how to make planners, professionals and politicians 'accountable' for their decisions, and how to involve the public in 'consultations' about them. This is the alternative to making providers responsive to empowered consumers, which can increase investment, capacity and self-responsibility.

It is an inadequate approach since the 'needs' model sets aside 'demand' (which otherwise would constitute the sums consumers might pay for specific services at current prices and incomes). Consumers may or may not be able to access a desired service. The effort to patch up the 'needs' model shows large intellectual, practical and fiscal deficits. Notably, that there is no consumer test of the value of each pound spent, no micro information on preferences, no information to test governmental claims about investment, and few exits for the individual. Those who can find a private provider they prefer pay twice as taxpayers and as private buyers. They cannot transfer the tax-payment to a competing supplier, if there is one.

There are no comparisons between competing services (seeking scarce resources) and competing suppliers. We have no measure of the value of services to the individual and their preferences, nor how to compare services, value for money, or relative desirability. These problems are what economists call the mismanagement of income and price-effects. The mismanagement has been by politicians, for political reasons.

Rationing in the 'needs' model makes the very large assumption that the necessary data can be known prior to decision by planners; that planners can know the correct or optimal mix of benefits, services, quantities, techniques, prices, providers, standards and relative competence of practitioners, together with the right mix of consumer-friendly behaviour and attitudes. In truth, these remain not merely to be discovered, but to be re-discovered constantly, in a market. The 'wants' model offers what Lord Harris has called 'the daily referendum in the market-place'. Here, 100 per cent of the 'sample' express their satisfactions, dissatisfactions and empowered wishes. The market, too, is not merely a technique, but part of a moral climate in which innovation, choice, spontaneity and unregimented order flourish.[3]

The NHS 'needs' model of care fails to explain widely varied practice, or why access to some treatments is more difficult in the UK than elsewhere. There are enormous variations in the treatment available and given in different parts of the UK. The 'needs' model does not explain these surprising and unexplained variations found in epidemiological studies, in practices apparently based on objective science. The complexity of medicine cannot explain why demand for services is higher in areas where there are more consultants, or why doctors can increase demand for services without clear evidence that outcomes improve. This over-supply is self-perpetuating. The availability of specialists generates demand for specialised care.[4] The NHS research director, Sir Michael Peckham, estimated that at least £1 billion a year could be saved by eliminating unnecessary treatments in the NHS. The *British National Formulary* also estimated that the NHS wastes more than £100 million on prescriptions 'of doubtful value', which Professor Alan Maynard said was an under-estimate.[5]

Jim Thornton, Reader in Obstetrics and Gynaecology at Leeds University, has recently commented:

> Relatively little of modern medicine is mandated by objective clinical justification. Most of it follows patient preferences and judgements and is more like a want ... Not all health care is a need. It is clear from people's behaviour that, as far as their own health goes, it is important but not an absolute priority. If it were, no one would smoke, drink, be sexually promiscuous, climb mountains or drive their car too fast.[6]

### The 'Market' Model

In the 'market' model, 'wants' are expressed by the individual. The patient considers prices and services. The amount and mix of care is chosen in the subjective light of personal preference and income or available personal insurance. Here, consumers are judged to be able to exercise judgement as to their own best interests. The assumption is that it is very difficult for anyone else to determine in advance what the best decisions comprise.

A shift away from needs to wants is the only way—in David Hume's terms—to access the true sources of morality and the process of discovery which Hayek describes. In a 'wants' model poor services, too, can be abandoned with manageable loss, unlike political (or public-sector) services for which voters exact a price, and which politicians fear.

Large sums are now spent on over-the-counter medicines, on alternative and complementary therapies, and on private insurance, even with its limited coverage. Many who have been said to be unable or unwilling to pay for services in a market are, clearly, ready to do so and are doing it when allowed to do so. This is, for them, an alternative to spending discretionary income on tobacco, alcohol, videos, white goods and holidays. The success of drop-in surgeries—the 'wants' model in action—is striking proof.

## *The Lessons of Drop-in GP Centres On Railway Stations*

Health care is viewed by government as a problem of government and of politics. Governments look at health from the point of view of government. They are especially concerned with constraining cost. However, consumers may wish to spend more, if they can get what they want when they want it. This may benefit the individual, the wider society, and the wealth-generating economy.

It is not clear that there is any objective way in which the right expenditure on health care can be decided. However, it seems that political control is inefficient, and that, if the wider European experience is any guide, health care consumption in Britain is fixed at too low a level for optimal care. However, if we irreducibly looked at health care from the point of view of the consumer, what might the system look like? What incentives might we privilege? How might a 'wants' model be realised? What might expenditures be, and how structured and funded?

An approach is clearly demonstrated by the success of the Medicentre drop-in GP (for-profit) service on railway stations, and in some branches of Boots and Sainsburys, run by Sinclair Montrose Healthcare. The centres are open 7.00 a.m. to 9.00 p.m., six days a week, with Sunday being considered as an option. This is a company which has started from the consumer's point of view, not from that of government. It has made the main objective to be the service people want, rather than that of hierarchy and control. This is a classic demonstration of what Hayek meant when he spoke of the process of discovery that price and commercial innovation uniquely offers. The project has been a specific test of what individuals would do with their own money (or insurance plans) if they could. Clearly, many are willing to spend money on what they want—as they do to the extent of £1,276 million annually on over-the-counter medicines without prescriptions, or some £50 a year for an average household. Some £500 million a year, too, is spent on alternative therapies. In the NHS, however, many pay taxes but cannot get the service.[7]

Many people—by no means all middle-class—pay £38 for a walk-in consultation, on a one-off basis. People are voluntarily supporting an alternative service, which is offered where and when they want it.[8] There is a direct economic measure of priced demand, and the possibility of existing supply being overtaken by new provision. The network of private family doctors, now being set up by PPP Healthcare Group, is a response to demand for a different level of service and convenience.[9]

There will soon be many such 'shops', situated where people want them and are prepared to pay for them. They may develop into primary care centres in the workplace, offering better information and more choice so that individuals can spend their own money on additional treatments. In Britain last year 200 million working days were lost in Britain because of illness, costing £12 billion in lost production, the main reasons being chronic illness.[10] Employers want a productive, fit, healthy workforce, and rapid, quality treatments. The NHS cannot presently meet this agenda. A state monopoly may never be able to accommodate wide choice. The questions then include how a consumer agenda might be met, and how can public and private be integrated.

A key question is to decide what the NHS should guarantee (if not necessarily provide). This could be a 'core service' guaranteed to all. The only way to address increasing consumer demands may be to fit the public and private sectors together well—the NHS, the pharmaceutical companies, the independent sector, the insurers, and mutual aid organisations. This might be done in an open and in an integrated way, and we need to study how.

We need, above all, to clarify consumer expectations and choices—what the state should and can fund, and what it should not do or fund. We must clarify what choices consumers have, and clarify how they can be funded and made real.

The argument between a 'needs' model and a 'wants' model concerns the importance of subjectivity as against 'objective' planning. The value we accord to 'subjectivity'—how we value it in health care—is at the heart of the problem of improving and investing in a more responsive health care structure which offers better care for all. The argument from the 'wants' model is that it is the individual who must be valued and that the wider society will benefit, too. Here, the pivot is good information, which becomes personal knowledge, with the individual having access to genuine leverage. Information is only one of the factors which are important to power. It has meaning only when it is considered in the context of empowering the individual, who is enabled to interpret a want and then to command a service for themselves. The challenge here is that information must mean something to the individual, and providers must supply it in the form consumers want, so that they can attract their money. This must be real money, not notional numbers, if health care staff are to look at the world of the service-buyer in a different way, and to respond in reality rather than in theory.

Kant urged that it is prior knowledge in the individual mind which is essential in decision-making. It is this prior knowledge which enables us to make information mean something. This, *de rigueur*, is to value the journey of personal discovery—what I later discuss as learning to choose—as the individual patient seeks a personal pattern of meaning, in making sense of disease and of what to do about it in their own lives. It is a personal sense of meaning which is unknowable by the standardising-and-centralising planner, acting on our behalf and in advance.

How information becomes knowledge for an individual, how it is 'processed' into meaningful ideas and personal understanding, is, of course, intrinsically subjective. It is the blend of prior knowledge, sensory experience, and individual response which is, too, the basis of self-responsibility. The NHS speaks of the importance of improving information. But the idea of 'information' by itself has no meaning. For without personal interpretation the raw material is merely a jumble of data. The value of information is entirely dependent on what the individual mind chooses to make of it. Personal *interpretation* is the crux of the matter. Being able then to secure a preferred service is the essential next step. This is the significance of the 'market' or 'wants' model.

There will, of course, be decisions made which to many may seem like logical failings. People will make choices we might not have made for ourselves—or which planners may not have made for us. Yet the value of the individual interpretation is that it reflects the commitment of the individual who must then take responsibility. The personal interpretation of data about choices conjures what is in the mind already—notably values and wishes of how to live. This is what we mean when we use the word 'subjective' and the word 'knowledge'. It is, too, precisely what the planner cannot 'know' on our behalf, as they seek to judge our wishes better than we do ourselves. In addition, it may be that we only truly 'know' our wishes when we face a real choice, when we have to take responsibility for an action. The individual brings to the task of interpretation a lifetime's unique experience and a particular cluster of personal values—all difficult for the planner to fathom in advance. These ingredients are the basic building blocks of what we call self-knowledge, and of self-responsibility.

The policy issue is how to behave so that an individual can achieve 'knowledge'—of course, in part guided by advocacy, by technical advice which helps the individual (as Charles Jonscher puts it) to guess 'right about what can go wrong'.[11] The result can then be the basis of genuine choices which contribute to social solidarity. Provided, that is, that there is the leverage to command a service. This is a necessary trinity of activities—data to information; information to knowledge; knowledge to leverage.

Then the challenge is for a service industry to obtain, satisfy and retain the customer. Here, as Porter implies, providers will require advertising (good information as well as persuasion), product positioning (serving particular wishes), and brand-building (creating satisfied and loyal customers with services of proven value). This structure is a prerequisite if investment, capacity and development are to happen at optimal rates.

The NHS has not yet recognised these truths. Its emphasis on the 'needs' model contradicts them. The many deficits in reported behaviours towards consumers who are not empowered as independent decision-takers are very telling and explicit. Nor has the NHS responded with comprehensive investment in the kinds of information systems which in the past 25 years have become commonplace in those industries—such as the airline business—where providers must serve the consumer or suffer the consequences. United Airlines, for example, typifies the commercial response to a similar business of volume demand at slim margins, with computer systems handling the profitable management of 160 million seats per annum on 850,000 flights. Yet as recently as 1998 the authoritative King's Fund annual review of health care policy devoted 13 of its scarce pages to the topic 'Should the NHS have a computing strategy?'[12]

By trusting to the pilot of the 'needs' model the NHS is not keeping up with what has been invented. It will be in much greater difficulty when soon confronted with what is still unknown, uninvented, and unavoidable—and which will require big steps if it is to keep up with the expectations seen as normal in the wider economy.

This challenge is now very obvious as we experience the technological transformation of society and of the economy. This is collapsing physical and psychological barriers, notably between providers and between purchasers in every industry. The surviving providers will be the organisations that tailor what they do to what the consumer seeks. Markets themselves are ceasing to be local and are indeed becoming international. Yet, unlike in the wider economy, British health care consumers are unable to select from amongst a greater variety of suppliers, judge products in new markets, or urge managements to respond to their wishes except by the insufficient interrogative of the vote. NHS investment is insufficient—in intellectual, in market and in financial terms. There is an inappropriate and out of date conceptual imagination. In a public-sector monopoly NHS managers still think of how to administer 'the budget'—a 'free good' which comes from nowhere—rather than to do work that earns the organisation real money by attracting willing demand from willing consumers who know they have a choice.

I have argued elsewhere[13] that the age of intelligent machines is already changing our relationship to ourselves—our concepts of who we are, and our ability to ask and answer questions in an international environment via the inter-connected clusters of personal computers on the Net in which we are all 'publishers' of our experiences as well as 'readers' of those of others. These machines, too, are learning to 'know' us, interact with us, and act on our behalf in the so-called 'natural interface technology'. They already seek out optimal solutions and present them for our consideration. They pass the initiative to the demand-side of service relationships. This is the new world which will come rapidly to health care. As home computers and patient contact evolves, our social institutions will have to respond. This imperative will require NHS administration to become management, and to shift from 'managing' budgets to seeking willing customers.

There is, too, a generational change. Our children will not readily accept what was 'obvious' to earlier generations, not least public-sector monopoly and the lack of choice. For they are already on-line to millions of data sources, which are intelligently analysed on their behalf by smart-machines. Indeed, it is a core concept of digital data that it can be analysed, accessed, and used for change—unlike much paper-based NHS filing, which enables management and professionals to side-step analysis and account-ability, and avoid those transparent imperatives which elsewhere require cost-reduction and improved performance. The digital developments we see are creative processes which can interpret the content of the data. Perhaps most importantly for the purposes of this re-consideration of the realities of rationing, these developments in the wider economy reveal that the challenge is *not* how to preserve the NHS, or how to buttress public-sector monopoly. It is instead how to evolve optimal health care services, of which the NHS might be part if it can respond in a new environment.

The 'needs' model will inevitably go to the wall, as part of the most extensive transformation of economy and society since the Enlightenment. Its most striking characteristic will be personal choice.

# 8

# Is Political Activism An Alternative To Financial Empowerment?

People say they would be prepared to pay higher taxes to pay for health care. But they have elected governments which have not increased taxes to achieve this. We thus face the alternatives of more political activism to enlarge funds, or the adoption of economic mechanisms. Let us consider these points.

### *Political Elections and Patient Preferences for Intimate, Personal Health Services*

The ballot box is a poor way to discover individual opinion about personal goods, about personal health benefits, about how and when the money is spent, about which services to buy and when. For the ballot box (and the health authority consultation) present alternatives without individual cost-consciousness about preferences. They offer no specific and individual leverage concerning particular and personal treatments. The opportunity, too, is only periodic. The process, offers choices which are no real alternatives, for they make no provision for the individual to express personal and cost-conscious choices about individual treatment preferences and outcomes. The political or strategic benefits, too, are often distant to the individual, and voting does not necessarily secure them. The vote does not fortify demand, nor necessarily enhance provision.

Voters are distanced, too, from budgeting and the precise mix of goods and services to be provided. Consultative methods to help determine local health spending are notoriously problematic. The citizen as voter is unable, for example, to secure more optimal investment in services. The citizen as shopper might, however, do so.

The political system has no means by which it can register the vastly different preferences of individuals. Voters 'select' a bundle of diverse, tax-financed goods and services periodically, with their preferences only being approximated at best. Rationing then proceeds to sort out what officials believe can be afforded, and for whom. As William Beveridge said, 'secession is the midwife of invention'.[1] However, individual patients who are dissatisfied cannot take their payments to another provider, or top-up with additional cash to purchase a preferred alternative from the public sector. They can only take part in consultation exercises and in priority setting processes (the most notable in Oregon, where democratic choices were made between alternative conditions that should be treated, ranked as priorities). The individual may indeed be *listened to* in consultations, but many doubt that they are being *heard*. And even if heard, they have no power to command a specific and timely personal benefit.

People can, of course, exert pressures, or ultimately seek to change the government. By then, however, the patient may be dead. For timeliness is of the essence. Most patients are concerned at an individual level—and often, rationally, only then—when they have a problem, since health care benefits are intimate and personal. Otherwise, many do not wish to be political activists. They wish to get on with their usual lives. In these terms participation is not necessarily progress, and many do not wish to participate; they want the service when they want it.

Here, Arthur Seldon has argued that the functioning of democracy itself suffocates the potential to discover what only economic mechanisms can reveal. Certainly, voting about 'values' does not give any leverage on specific services. It does nothing to register consumer wants where individuals could know cost, quality, price and who could make the necessary trade-offs made in other areas of ordinary life. As the European Union develops it may, too, become increasingly difficult to change policy by voting to change government, with Britain being a minority within a diverse majority. Health care, too, may eventually be harmonised, if political union becomes a reality, despite the very diverse health care structures presently seen in Europe.

None of the many thousands whose complaints were counted in the NHS League Tables published in December 1998 were able to go elsewhere with their tax-funds.[2] The individual losses which might be made up in a market system are concealed, too, in the figures. A complaint is aggregated as 'a problem'. However, the individual cannot hit back, transfer to a better service, encourage an alternative, or, in most cases, seek a second opinion.

As Seldon commented:

> An indispensable element of reform is to return the judgement of risk from the political process, where it is chronically over-estimated by politicians anxious to enlarge government, to the informed experience of individuals, families, fraternal groups, with a common interest in everyday private life who bear the consequences of their misjudgments but who learn from experience how to judge and to minimise risks.[3]

## The Delusion of The Opinion Poll

This device is much loved by vested interests, often posing as the national interest. It must be treated with caution, and not taken at face value.

Opinion polls regularly report two things: that people are passionate about the NHS, and that people want taxes increased to modernise the NHS. But such polls—even the sophisticated ones conducted by the British Social Attitudes survey, and by MORI for the Social Market Foundation—have no cost to the respondent, since individuals do not have to support their opinion with their own money. It is painless to say you would vote for someone else to pay the taxes when responding to an unpriced survey which emphasises 'compassion' but ignores the economic truth that there is no demand without a price. Those 'sampled' are never told what the costs will be of the extra services or what the opportunity costs would be. Nor do these polls necessarily add 'voice', since they are not linked to financial leverage to enable people to command the service. The tax demanded is unspecific, so there is no opportunity to pay more for health *qua* health. A hypothecated tax would be a step towards a direct link between the individual, lifestyle and consumption, if it stressed that benefits would be earned by contributions, and that these would be guaranteed. This would be a step towards market economics, based on competition and choice, but these virtues are not encouraged by government in health care. The difficulty would remain that individual benefits cannot be specified or selected by tax alone.

However, the essential micro-information and the market signals uniquely expressed by price (and which concern intimate, timely, and personal services) cannot be gathered by government. It cannot be done either in voting, in 'consultations' or by so-called refined methods of discovering individual preference such as citizens' juries. These, indeed, insidiously seek to achieve something entirely different. This is to 'educate' the patient, 'enabling them' to understand the problems of management in rationing inadequate finances. They do so while trying to predict the free will that motivates supply and demand, which prompts money for investment, more risks to be taken, more innovations made.

Stephen Thornton, Chief Executive of the NHS Confederation, recently suggested that a question on rationing should be included in the government's forthcoming national attitudes survey, as little is known of public views of rationing. However, this comment reflected the misunderstanding that surveys without prices give useful information, whereas we have seen they offer no cost-conscious information which is useable in responding to demands. Without price and individual cost-consciousness we cannot discover what the optimal level of funding might be to achieve the desired level of production and the correction of the deficits in the state system of health provision.

The proposed NHS annual survey of patient opinion may be helpful in revealing some anecdotal stories. But it will not have the impact of the daily referendum of the market. It is another uncosted survey, with no cost-conscious choices offered. There is no information offered, either, by which respondents to such a survey can inform themselves on such vital issues as which doctors to trust, and on what other patients report—even for the limited choices open to patients.

### The Illusion of Citizens' Juries

This is a recent innovation to renew the political direction of health services. It does nothing to reform incentive or encourage competition and innovation. It treats symptoms, not underlying causes. It increases regulation, while failing to improve quality or increase services. It is a substitute which seeks to match what can be learned from free-market mechanisms. Citizens' juries ignore the economic truth that demand rises when prices fall or when quality at a given price increases. They seek instead to make the NHS 'fairer', by 'involving' the public in evaluating the different claims and by laying down rules on what can and cannot be provided.

This is part of the process of inquiry, verification, control, and regulation which officialdom requires as the basis of value judgements about service provision. It exemplifies the planner's dilemmas in seeking to predict (and regulate) demand for services in advance. First, the impossibility of discovering individual future preferences if you do not empower markets with information, price and finance. Second, the impossibility of aggregating spontaneous individual decisions, except by market mechanisms. Third, the failures that arise from placing the inefficiencies of government decision ahead of private decision and responsibility.

Citizens' juries give a small number of unelected individuals (who become part of the corporate politics of the NHS) an insight, and perhaps a 'say' in what can be done and what afforded. The process seeks to 'educate' the public to 'understand'. As with the NHS complaints system, this often means a process whereby people are instructed on why things must be the way that they are.

Citizens' juries are thus one mechanism by which managers can reshuffle the order of what is in the basket and—as in Oregon's more 'democratic' rationing process—discard some items which should not be paid for. They do not confront the fundamentals of engaging the individual in priced decision-making, nor promote mechanisms to create greater funding and capacity. They offer a political substitute for the grounds of moral decision-making and of the moral development of the self-responsible individual urged by David Hume.

Such 'juries' are no substitute for a market. They help continue instead the situation where there is no real and direct test of cost-consciousness, and of who would pay what for which services. Like voting, they focus much less power than the expression of consumer wants. Citizens' juries suggest that we can 'know how things are' on behalf of others. Thus, citizens' juries offer a 'theory of knowledge'. Yet, fundamentally, they make impossible demands upon our knowledge—as do all interventionist policies which discount markets. They help undermine the dignity of the individual, the moral primacy of freedom, and the necessity of limited government under the framework of law. For this is the impact of the system of ideas citizens' juries reflect.

In brief, there is a binary choice: is the patient to determine preferred levels of care by a life of activist politics—planning, consultation, strategic thinking, with each of us becoming a politician—or by economics, in selecting a health care plan which will guarantee specific services when they are wanted?

P.J. O'Rourke puts it neatly: 'Money is preferable to politics. It is the difference between being free to be anybody you want and being free to vote for anybody you want'.[4] Milton Friedman, too, wrote that 'if economic power is joined to political power, concentration seems almost inevitable. On the other hand, if economic power is kept in separate hands from political power, it can serve as a check and a counter to political power'.[5]

This understanding of the necessary connection between speaking and spending, the alternative to voice and vote, stresses the personal rather than the political. It highlights the private choice, as against the decisions of a 'disinterested' élite occupied with undistracted reason. It privileges character, independence, individuality, personal responsibility, initiative, and self-reliance, by contrast with millennial activism and grandiose political schemes. The vote itself (for all its clear benefits) may be more than ineffective as a method of expressing health care choices. For it prompts a vote-buying democracy. Democracy and liberty are not quite the same thing, as Plato said, although they are often juxtaposed. One is a method, the other a principle. The one can corrode the other.

As Alan Duncan and Dominic Hobson have said:

> It is in the nature of the democratic political system that a majority will always be voting to expropriate the property of a minority without their consent...Political choices will always differ from market choices, in that they cannot be made with the agreement of all the parties.[6]

There is, too, no known political mechanism or planning strategy which can summarise all preferences as one preference.

In the NHS we have no way of assessing how much additional money people individually would like to spend on health care. Political mechanisms tell us less than economic mechanisms which give specific influence to individuals. 'Democratising' choice may be insufficient without economic democracy. The power, too, of medical and political authorities over consumers remains entrenched, and reliance on taxation alone remains unreliable. The price-less allocation system submerges the relative cost of alternative services and suppliers. It avoids discovering what effect extra resources controlled by individuals would have if based on preferences for different timing, location, choice of surgeon, of treatment, facilities, preferred outcome, care-plan.

There are several choices offered by which funding could grow, perhaps on a broader base. These include an NHS funded exclusively from higher taxation; a service mainly funded by taxation, but with the support of expanded charges; a service funded in part from taxation and in part from an independent insurance element; or services funded from compulsory insurance as an entire funder.

Whichever approach is selected, 'there is,' as David Green has written, 'no escape from cost-consciousness. We face a choice between, on the one hand, the cost-conscious paternalism of the medical and political authorities, and on the other, cost-conscious personal choice. Effective consumer choice is only possible if it is accompanied by consumer payment'.[7] This is the necessary basis of a re-definition of social and economic values in health care.

# 9

# Self-responsibility and Competition

Self-responsibility is the third principle problem of rationing in a public-sector monopoly. It—and the necessity of competition—is pivotal to the entire discussion. Michael Porter has said:

> Very few industries remain in which competition has not intruded on stability and market dominance. No company, and no country, can afford to ignore the need to compete. Every company, and every country, must try to understand and master competition.[1]

Yet the NHS assumes that competition is a disadvantage. It remains underpinned by the assumption of the primacy of the public sector and the state as the source of morality. The alternative presented in this essay of how health services could be funded, organised and delivered is fundamentally based in a moral view. This concerns the characteristics of a society of freedom, liberty and the routes to self-responsibility. A principal difficulty is the idea that the NHS has of the individual as someone with a role, to be directed by a remedial government or its agents.

The alternative to the NHS perception is the ideal of Robert Nozick's 'self-owned' individual.[2] The libertarian contrast is with the individual as someone with a moral compass, a character, and with self-respect. This idea offers the moral autonomy of the man within, guided by beliefs and preferences. This is to seek the basis of a society in which we each carry in our lived lives the values of the community in mutual responsibility. It is the account that David Green has offered, to re-invent civil society in a 'community without politics'.[3] Here there would be a strong voluntary, not-for-profit sector purchasing and providing health services. Such a society would be concerned with how to assure good health care for all, with protection for the weak.

Such a notion is, however, displaced by the political structure and assumptions of the NHS. This is the cause of much of its difficulty with rationing. For the NHS fails to respect the individual whom it should be expected to protect and support to take an individual part in responsible membership in a civil society. Instead of highlighting the central virtue of self-command and innate moral sense, the state affects instead a Hobbesian view that people are bad and must be controlled by government. Or that people are victims, to be compensated. Unfortunately, each of these ideas has released people from self-responsibility, to their own disadvantage both as moral beings and as health consumers. It is a genuine concern that a service which sought to express a moral view has itself encouraged a moral vacuum.

The historian David Howarth has persuasively written that 'absolute personal freedom ... has always been a dangerous illusion'. And, indeed, that we should seek 'the acceptance of the duties and mutual support of a social system'.[4] Advocates of changes in financing and in power-relations stress this view. For the concern is not merely with a society of untrammelled individual irresponsibility, but of mutuality where 'collectivism' is redefined non-politically.

In the NHS the role of the individual is not only too limited, too distrusted, too marginal. It is a coerced role, within which the NHS finds it must ration information, personal discretion and room for judgement. The NHS asks people to fit *its* requirements, which has restricted its ability to ensure greater awareness of the links between behaviour, lifestyle, and health status, which could prevent up to 80 per cent of all breast and bowel cancers, for example. It has generated its own difficulty with regard to 'responsible consumption', since it has no moral framework on which to rely which is genuinely connected to the real sources of self-respect. The distrusted individual is asked to refuse to consume what he has been promised free (and which has been a test of his worthiness and 'rights' in a welfare system).[5] This practical and moral quandary is self-created. It stands in contrast to NHS declarations about humanity. The sources of self-government, self-improvement, self-responsibility, self-help, innovation and spontaneity, diversity and individuality lie elsewhere.

Vital in this debate is the displacement effect of the state which has narrowed the scope of individual conscience and responsibility and the moral opportunities open to individuals. It has done so by substituting a role for the individual as taxpayer for a role as responsible individual. One important recusant step is to re-discover the submerged mechanisms for expressing these ideas. The revival of voluntarist organisations of mutual aid, and of lost history crowded out by the state in 1948, seems to offer much. For in voluntarist organisations people set personal money aside in a common fund, helping themselves, their families and one another in an independent organisation which they felt was 'theirs'. These self-help organisations expressed the spontaneous aspirations of those on lower incomes. They were enabled to buy mutual and commercial 'industrial' insurance against sickness, unemploy-ment, old age and the other unavoidable—but measurable, and insurable—risks of life.

The societies were, too, a moral engine—and a part of an old and extensively-subscribed tradition of Labour. They inculcated restraint, self-help, duty, virtue and moral-discipline. Patients shared information about the relative capacities of doctors, and this protective power was valued. The mutual aid clubs exercised financial power directly on behalf of the medical consumer who was a willing subscriber in a market of alternative mutual aid organisations seeking his business. This financial power was used to buy preferred treatments, as well as influencing directly the pay, status, and conditions of many professionals. No NHS patient has that power today. It was lost in the nationalisation of health services which began in 1911 with the National Insurance Act.

The self-financing organisations of mutual aid represented a non-collectivist response to the risks of life. They were outstand-ing examples of working-class self-help, and provided comprehen-sive insurance plans for sickness, unemployment, age and infirmity, medical care and burial. William Beveridge, indeed, wanted them retained, and particularly valued them for their continued experimentation.[6]

# 10

# Are We Living in Modern Times?

The problems evidently clustered around 'rationing' in health care are fundamental, structural and systemic. They directly affect the scarcest of all resources—the days of our lives.

There are, of course, many who affect to believe that what is, must always be. E.L. Doctorow offers a warning here: 'You may think you are living in modern times, here and now, but that is the necessary illusion of every age'.[1] It is a major political and professional challenge instead to reconcile the present with the past, to enable the necessary future to emerge. One in which individuals make decisions about rationing and priorities for themselves, self-responsibly, on their own terms. As the French say, *autres temps, autres moeurs*.

The discussion of possible change in public policies has not, of course, been confined to classical liberals. Notably from the left, Anthony Giddens has offered an analysis of the consequences of modernity and of changing relationships to traditional attitudes and social forms which seems to me to be directly relevant.[2] This analysis is very helpful in considering what to do about health care funding, capacity and self-responsibility. It relates directly to our need to sort out which of our traditions and beliefs remain useful, which obstruct necessary change, which are adaptable and how.

I have argued that it is fundamental to be guided by the sources of morality, value and knowledge, and that those offered in health care by the present public-sector monopoly of the NHS are both historical and inappropriate. They have a life that was embedded in past space and time, to use a phrase that recurs in Giddens' work. They are an insufficient guide to what to do now, as we seek to manage the risks and opportunities we confront individually and collectively. Here, self-knowledge, self-responsibility, open negotiation and exchange—what Giddens calls 'self-actualisation', or realising one's identity through personal and social encounters —are re-emerging as moral and practical alternatives to traditional roles and norms. These norms have been expressed in hierarchy, bureaucracy and control—in John Vincent's words, as 'instruments for excluding the chaos of public opinion'.[3] These instruments are increasingly questionable, as we seek to develop better health care for all—in markets which are not chaotic, but which are highly structured.

Giddens discusses how to enhance social cohesion in a post-socialist, post-modernist world. The classical liberal view is that social cohesion is dependent on individualism, in the freshness and with the purchase offered by Green's 'community without politics'. I have argued for the re-definition of collectivism which will secure individual benefits within a social structure. Giddens himself says: 'We can have a morality that is both social, in a certain sense collective, but that also recognises the key significance of individual freedom'.[4]

Giddens has argued for a new 'life politics [which] concerns life decisions. It is a politics of choice, identity and mutuality'.[5] Further, it is the role of government to 'regulate markets in the public interest and foster market competition where monopoly threatens'.[6] He has identified a series of shifts which define modernity. These involve challenges to tradition, custom and habit in a multiplicity of respects. In each, old institutions have lost their resonance. Each is directly relevant to the approach to changing health care which has been argued in this essay.

He suggests that several old categories have dissolved: these include the discrediting of Marxism, of the economic programme of socialism, and of the welfare consensus that was accepted in all industrial countries (save the USA) until the late 1970s. There is, he says, no longer a socialist alternative to capitalism. Globalisation, too, 'is not only or even primarily about economic interdependence, but about the transformation of time and space in our lives'.[7] This 'pulls away' from the nation-state; it 'pushes down' too, creating new demands which impact, for example, on service providers.

A key element of modernity has been a changing of attitudes to what is accepted in relationships. There has been a renewed emphasis on autonomy and on lifestyle diversity—in open homosexuality, in the movement towards single-sex marriages, in increasing sexual equality and changing relationships at work and at home. There have been widespread changes in attitudes towards hierarchy and control, including, notably, a post-modernist challenge to the professions, whose prestige has declined: 'Experts cannot be relied upon automatically to know what is good for us, nor can they always provide us with unambiguous truths; they should be called upon to justify their conclusions and policies in the face of public scrutiny'.[8]

We are all, too, living in a more saturated, and shared, information environment. Everyone is getting access to information. This is querying pre-given modes of conduct and is a key element in changing the situation of the professions. Distant events and actions have a constant effect on our lives. Expert knowledge systems—once marked off in special code—are breaking open to new inter-actions. I have analysed this via the world wide web.

All this is a dynamic social order, which 'unlike any preceding culture lives in the future rather than the past'.[9] One important aspect of this shift of respect, the renewal of intimacy, and the decline in the power of myth (which may, to some extent, threaten the beneficial and therapeutic yield of faith) is that we have to reconsider our attitudes to managing risk. Giddens says that 'risk assessment can't simply be placed in the hands of scientific experts. All forms of risk calculation and coping strategy imply a consideration of values and desired ways of life. They also have a critical bearing on systems of power and vested interests'.[10] The assessment and management of risk is fundamental to learning to choose. Giddens has his own phrase for this—'the development of cognitive and emotional competence'. Hayek calls this 'learning to choose'. Thackeray called it 'consciousness', pointing out that anyone's experience, accurately seen, is distinct and individual; that 'it is only hope which is real'; and that '[a] distinct universe walks under your hat and under mine'.[11]

There is no alternative but to manage, share and spread risk. The question is who is to do this and how. As Giddens points out, risk can be energising for the individual and for society as well as threatening. His view is:

> Once tradition and nature are transformed, forward-looking decisions have to be taken, and we have responsibility for their consequences. Who should bear responsibility for the future consequences of present activities (whether of individuals, nations or other groups) is one of the major concerns of the new politics, as is who provides security if things go wrong, how and with what resources ... We all need protection against risk, but also the capability to confront and take risks in a productive fashion.[12]

In finding answers, however, we do not need to accept his approach in its entirety. We should not confuse 'community' with the 'public sector'. We would not sustain monopolies which level down, nor under-estimate (as he does) the value of the family as a moral institution.

Instead, as I have argued, we should re-define collectivism to benefit from the new autonomy we see around us in our social relations. We should do so in a changed balance of mutual obligation, self-responsibility and risk management. This is the territory of what Giddens calls 'the new individualism'. But it should not be ceded to paternalism and a revivified central state.

We need to re-consider risk (and responsibility)—and who can manage it best—in confronting a more open future for the individual. Risk need not necessarily be nationalised. Here, professionals, politicians and patients alike need to educate themselves about the nature of risk, which is the assessment of future hazards. Government is not necessarily the only insurer of risk. It would seem that we are all in fact more attuned to and accepting of risk as we make complex decisions in our lives compared with the 1940s. As Giddens says:

> Risk has to be separated from hazard or danger. Risk is about the active assessment of future hazards, and becomes a more pervasive notion the more a society seeks to live in the future and shape it actively. The concept of risk becomes generalised with the rise of modernity, as does the idea of insurance. Insurance and safety are the other side of risk.[13]

Giddens argues that:

> Social cohesion can't be guaranteed by the top-down action of the state or by appeal to tradition. We have to make our own lives in a more active way than was true of previous generations, and we need more actively to

accept responsibilities for the consequences of what we do and the lifestyle habits we adopt. The theme of responsibility, or mutual obligation, was there in old-style social democracy, but was largely dormant, since it was submerged within the concept of collective provision. We have to find a new balance between individual and collective responsibilities today ... All of us have to live in a more open and reflective manner than previous generations. This change is by no means only a beneficial one, new worries and anxieties come to the fore. But many more possibilities do, too.[14]

Classical liberals would be comfortable with this release of subjectivity, expressed in self-responsibility. But not with his idea of 'negotiated order', by which he means an increase of activism as an alternative to the cumulate gains from the impact of practical and individual decisions in the market. His preference for increased political activism—electronic referenda, citizens' juries—is less persuasive, since economic power is more directly persuasive than political voting, similarly, the leftist idea of 'contestability', or judgement by some 'assessor' within the system. For this, too, is a substitute for direct accountability to the consumer.

We have seen that more political activism does not equate with better services. It is a major difficulty, too, that it is politicians themselves who must collaborate in reforming politics. Giddens himself notes that consumers' rights have fallen outside traditional social democratic politics, and civil and political rights have often been merely formal. As he says, this has been dependent 'upon backstage deals, privilege and patronage', and 'the culture of secrecy that has pervaded the higher levels of British institutions'.[15]

The direction of travel expressed by Giddens is helpful, too, to the Hayekian Whig when he says:

In the positive welfare society, the contract between individual and government shifts, since autonomy and the development of self—the medium of expanding individual responsibility—become the prime focus. Welfare in this basic sense concerns the rich as well as the poor. Positive welfare would replace each of Beveridge's negatives with a positive: in place of Want, autonomy; not Disease, but active health; instead of Ignorance, education, as a continuing part of life; rather than Squalor, well-being; and in place of Idleness, initiative.[16]

He also argues that:

The furthering of individual autonomy and self-esteem in everyday life should be regarded as just as important a political task as legal and other freedoms in the public sphere. These are to an extent the condition of those freedoms.[17]

However, in the NHS, we notice, by contrast, the cultural and contextual nature of the language so often used—'partnership', 'involvement', 'consultation'. This reflects the old consciousness which represents and re-states the public-sector realities of the denial of autonomy. These marginalise subjectivity. They re-affirm hierarchy, rigid and disciplinary traditional habits and forms of behaviour. They determine the taken-for-granted expectations between patient and professional. This is the picture of Foucault's 'docile body'.

It is basic to notice such fundamentals as these relationships between the patient and the NHS system at many diverse points. These practical sociologies crucially concern relationships of power and expectation—the context within which relationships and expectations are expressed, of oneself and of others. Careful observation of them is a beginning for the preparation for the effort to change the inheritance of relationships encoded by time and space, by expectation and behaviour in our institutions, habits and practices. As one commentator on the work of Giddens has said:

Conversational rules, behavioral expectations or intimate interpersonal rituals, for example, are embedded in knowledge about how and why social life happens: who speaks or is silent and when, who stands or sits and why, who belongs or does not and where, who is revered or reviled and how...[18]

—what Giddens calls '"the practical sociologies" that people use without, usually, consciously thinking about them'. It is these patterns of perception which need to be seen and changed, as with so much that is 'obvious' and received but which is neither the only possibility nor necessarily the best hope.

Berlin offered the basis for true freedom and responsibility, with its tolerance of diversity and respect for individuality:

I wish my life and decisions to depend on myself, not on external forces of whatever kind. I wish to be the instrument of my own, not of other men's, acts of will. I wish to be a subject, not an object; to be moved by reasons, by conscious purposes, which are my own, not by causes which affect me, as it were, from outside. I wish to be somebody, not nobody; a doer-deciding, not being decided for, self-directed and not acted upon by external nature or by other men as if I were a thing, or an animal, or a slave incapable of playing a human role, that is, of conceiving goals and policies of my own and realising them.[19]

This Lockeian aspiration shows how far the individual is from Berlin's ideal of self-respect and self-responsibility. And how far the system is from benefiting from what Mill, in his peroration in closing *On Liberty*, applauded as 'the vital power' of individual exertion and development.[20] The distance to be travelled is considerable, if funding, capacity, and self-responsibility are to coincide.

No one suggests that these will be easy changes to achieve. Major changes in any system—even one which subjugates and denies its own clients—are always deeply unsettling. However, as John Wyndham once noted, 'it is surprising how often the better thing is disguised as the worse'.[21]

There will, of course, be problems whichever system of finance and delivery we adopt. The question is what problems can we best live with, to make which gains? A libertarian view would say that self-responsibility, freedom and liberty are moral and social values which should not be compromised. And, thus, a system which fortifies demand would be in place. A collectivist would wish to privilege equality, wealth re-distribution, and equity. The NHS is the model that results, but it does not meet its objectives. Sanctification is not necessarily supply; epic solace is insufficient without intimate, individual service.

Health care cannot be separated from its moral environment. But it seems that the collectivist approach works least well, with the least positive impact on the self-responsibility of the individual, and on services made available. Instead, the moral principles which should guide us are those described by Michael Novak in three inter-dependent sets of institutions or systems:

> *a democratic polity* (limited government under the rule of law, protection of rights, checks and balances, etc.); *a capitalist economy* (with more stress on enterprise and invention than on the three pre-capitalist features: markets, private property, and accumulation); *a culture that nourishes the*

*habits*, (social and individual, required by free societies). That is, those institutions that seem from trial and error to be the necessities for a society that wishes to be free, and that hopes to sustain high standards of necessary services for all.[22]

The engines of success require equal justice under the law, equality of opportunity and of status. These are not the same notions as that expressed by the idea of equality, and which, as Alexis de Tocqueville, James Madison and Novak himself noted, tends to smother the idea of liberty.

The objective is that those who do least well can do much better in a free society than in an unfree one, and that they can learn the skills and be financially motivated and empowered so to do. We can 'carry our own weight', as independent and creative, civic-minded individuals. Novak says that: 'The citizen belongs to the class of sovereigns, the possessors of ultimate power. In the free society, the principal repository of power is the personal responsibility of citizens'.[23] As John Lloyd notes: 'We are faced not with a choice between welfare and no welfare, but between different kinds'.[24]

Despite Hayek's reservations about state regulation, the state has a key role to play in ensuring that creative, supportive structures emerge. These can spread the benefits of market competitiveness, reduce dependencies, and enlarge funding, capacity, and self-responsibility. We can each take much more responsibility for living our own lives, face and manage risk, and raise our conduct to the level of the moral and the deliberate, guided by our own moral compass and with a commitment in duty to others.

### Opening the Doors: Learning To Choose In a Competitive World

This is where the doors can open wide to a revised structure which empowers social, economic and health care objectives together. E.L. Doctorow says something helpful here: 'The way enlightenment comes ... is in bits and pieces of humdrum reality, each adding its mosaic bit of glitter to the eventual vision'.[25] Hayek famously puts this point:

[I]t is in the process of learning, and in the effects of having learned something new, that man enjoys the gift of his intelligence ... It is knowing what we have not known before that makes us wiser men ...What matters is the successful striving for what at each moment seems attainable ... it is the living in and for the future in which human intelligence proves itself.[26]

Hayek suggested, with Aristotle and Adam Smith, that we acquire virtues by exercising them. We do so in assessing the unavoidable uncertainties of life. He emphasised, too, the vibrant potential of our human character to live self-directed lives in which we daily challenge ourselves to develop our talents, virtues and conditions. This is the alternative to a situation where the state manages us and our affairs, in exchange for taxes, 'caring' for us, as an adult to a child.

We need to recover learning to choose. This involves the essential of learning to adjust to others and to cope with our own selves. This matters for many fundamental reasons, even if people make some choices for themselves which we might not make for ourselves. It includes learning the necessities of foresight, self-command, self-rationing and self-denial. Thus, the market is a moral education, in which we recognise rules which apply to others, embodying mutual respect. It is not merely a process of exchange without a moral setting.

The presence of many people learning to choose, and with the power of exit in a market, has other valuable effects. These include the development of independent advisory services, counselling and advocacy, and the process of continuous discovery to ratchet up performance and exert pressure on standards and productivity.

Ultimately, the physical assets of the NHS should be converted, perhaps re-voluntarised, given back to the local community, as not-for-profit local charitable trusts as with many hospitals in Europe. This would transfer the responsibility for the renewal of assets from the public ('political') domain to local ownership, the only basis for local control, competitive provision and innovation. There would remain a framework of regulation for quality and service standards. The state would remain important in such a programme of change, but it would be restricted to upholding what Green has called 'the protected domain of initiative which *is* liberty'.[27]

Whatever we do, we cannot get it all. Berlin has told of us of the problems of incommensurables. And, as David Green has written:

> One of the most important lessons of history is that there is no perfection in human affairs. The human condition is to struggle for improvement and, once we have made discoveries or learnt lessons, to struggle again to prevent hard-won lessons from being forgotten. We never know what the future holds and for this reason we should make arrangements which speed up the process by which we learn from experience. Public-sector monopoly acts on the exactly contrary principle. It assumes there is one obvious right answer and that the state can achieve the desired outcome most effectively. The history of state welfare exactly illustrates the folly of such an assumption.[28]

The NHS is caught between the tides of central direction and responsiveness to the individual. It is caught between the ideas of different generations, between gaps in understandings and expectations of the fate people seek for themselves. This difficulty itself encapsulates its problems of finance and capacity.

There is a time lag in the public comprehension of events and their meaning. But there is evidence that demand is now over-whelmingly overtaking supply. Reality is now catching up with the situation, with the advantages of a public-sector monopoly seemingly becoming clearly outweighed by the disadvantages. Change is unavoidable, and it needs to be carefully managed to allow a system of competitive free enterprise to emerge whilst the state guarantees cover for all.

There will be those who reject the suggestions of this essay as idealism, as utopian in the current 'climate of opinion'. However, Edwin J. Feulner, Jnr. has pointed out that those on the left have habitually proceeded by 'contrasting the existing state of affairs with that one ideal of a possible future society',[29] and that it is the responsibility of liberals to offer genuine alternatives. We must hold up in the public eye a vision of a future society built on liberty; the strange exception that has been made for health care looks increasingly inappropriate. As John Blundell has com-mented, we must 'look for leverage for tomorrow', and believe in the power of ideas.[30]

This was always Hayek's message, that we are governed by the power of ideas, and it is these which can change lives. We should not compromise freedom, for this is the realm of politicians and not of those who seek to think through the problems. However, this essay offers practical ways to make advances, rooted both in consistent liberal principles which help us organise the understanding of what we observe around us and which open new horizons. The essay, I believe, offers close observation of the daily facts and realities of rationing in the NHS, and, as a contrast, the state of affairs that could emerge—and which, indeed, has emerged in contemporary European countries where inequalities of health care are less and the quality of services is superior. We do not need to rely on imagination, nor even rely on 'the courage to be Utopian'. We can actually see most of the changes proposed in practice already, in Germany, Holland, and elsewhere.

It would be a surprise, and a disadvantage, if there were universal agreement. These are difficult problems for which no one has a complete blueprint or a final truth. Further experience of managing change will itself produce new ideas from others. However, there will always be those who seek to exercise a censorship function against change. As Blundell says, 'Experts in particular fields often gain "rents" from state intervention, and while overtly free-market in their outlook elsewhere, are always quick to explain why the market does not work in their area'.[31] Medical professionals frequently fly this flag. It is often difficult to find disinterested support for changes which lead to greater freedoms for all. Hayek makes the point: 'Those who are most familiar with the working of the present society are also usually interested in the preservation of particular features of that society which may not be defensible on general principles'.[32]

The general theme has been that deliberate control in social affairs is not superior to the spontaneous processes of society, and that a plan laid down in advance is not necessarily better than one formed by dynamic developments led by preferences in a system of priced-demand. Contemporary European experience demonstrates that the funding, capacity and self-responsibility in health care can be much improved by a broader commitment to markets as the lynch-pin of liberty and of improved services to the individual. All goods, ultimately, are rationed. It is best when this is explicit—nature rations us all—and undertaken by the individual concerned. Public-sector monopoly makes the situation worse for everyone, as it does the moral relations between individuals. The key problem certainly looks as if it is one of primary distribution of good services, rather than of redistribution. The ultimate question remains who decides who decides.

Meanwhile, rationing persists and patient empowerment is profoundly remote. In addition, the recently retired senior Department of Health official who wrote the 'official' 50th anniversary history said: 'The NHS may provide better value for money than most other systems—but it is often too little, too late'. The investment in NICE (The National Institute for Clinical Excellence) may, too, hit the usual buffers. For, as its Chairman designate, Sir Michael Rawlins, (whilst denying that he was engaged in rationing) has said, 'It's no good us recommending therapy if there isn't the money available'. [33]

On hearing of the death of Napoleon Bonaparte on St. Helena, Prince Talleyrand is said to have commented: 'Not an event; just news'. It is Viagra which has put rationing so dramatically back into the news. But rationing is more than news. It is the fundamental pathology of the present NHS system.

# Who Is Responsible, Who Is To Blame?
## A General Practitioner's Perspective
## on the Realities of Rationing

### A Personal View
# Bob Gilbertson

## 1. Rationing Can Be Valuable

Financial restraint has been a discipline which has stimulated much that is good in British general practice. Limited funds have forced choices to be made about where future resources are used and a constant review of the current use of those resources. Most important of all, limited funds raise the question of how these choices should be made and by whom.

### Who Should Make the Decisions?

Since the establishment of the National Health Service (NHS) in 1948,[1] accountability for the use of NHS funds has been devolved from the Department of Health first to regional authorities, and more recently to health authorities. In primary care, the gatekeeper role of the general practitioner (GP) and the issue of clinical freedom have created a tension within the system.

Fundholding in a limited way passed the accountability to individual practices or to groups of practices forming 'multifunds'. The implementation of the 1997 white paper on the future of the NHS[2] will increasingly place accountability with the newly established primary care groups (PCGs) or trusts.

Some practices have seen fundholding as an opportunity to involve patients directly in decisions about how resources are used. The Patient Participation Group (PPG) in our practice had a fascinating debate precipitated by the health authority's very reasonable desire to distribute limited funds for chiropody more equally between practices. This meant a reduction in the chiropody component of the Hospital Services Fund. As a fundholding practice, funds could have been redirected from other hospital services to maintain the unrestricted service then offered in the practice. Although some members of the PPG were personally aware of what a reduction in the chiropody service would mean to older members of their own families, they were not prepared to advise the inevitable reduction of other services.

The decision to create and fund a national health service was political. Responsibility for this and decisions about the proportion of tax revenue allocated to the NHS is decided at the ballot box. The separation of these decisions from the consequences of how the voters use their NHS, expecting as a 'right' unlimited care, is a major weakness of the system.

## Rationing Forces Review

The fact that resources are limited is inescapable. This reality has provided motivation for addressing how the limited funds can best be used in primary care. Current ways of providing the service have been reviewed and different ways of meeting needs and targets have been developed. While cost-effectiveness may have been the initial motivation, frequently the debate itself and the utilisation of new technology have also enhanced the quality of the care. Certainly it has led to the development of new skills throughout the primary health care team, including the general practitioners (GPs), the nurses and other members of staff, both within and attached to practices. Finally, rationing justifies economy and applies pressure to eliminate waste.

### Rationing Forces a Review of the Way Care Is Provided

GP prescribing, of all activities in primary care, is perhaps the most readily available for audit. Audits of prescribing do demonstrate a response to financial restraint. That large potential savings still remain to be made also make it of particular interest.

Prescribing habits of GPs continue to be modified, with the percentage of drugs prescribed generically rising. It is hard to explain the significant difference in this percentage between fundholders and non-fundholders and its beneficial impact on prescribing costs in any other terms than motivation to reduce spending.[3] With the end of fundholding there must be anxiety that the savings in drug costs achieved will begin to be eroded unless this motivation for individual prescribers is maintained. The great emphasis on clinical governance in the new primary care groups (PCGs) is an attempt to do this.

Our practice has also seen an increase, as have many others, in the use of protocols of care for chronic disease. This has significantly reduced the need for specialist advice and for hospital admission when a condition becomes unstable. Asthma and diabetes protocols have had a measurable impact on hospital admission rates. The NHS's ability to measure outcomes is in its infancy, its traditional focus being on input. If this weakness were remedied, the results could be used with considerable effect.

Combining health resources from several currently separate funds may also offer an opportunity for economic rationalisation. It is timely that the 1997 white paper begins to address this issue. However, the outcome measured must take no account of the increasingly artificial barriers between primary and secondary care. The measure must also be sensitive to the inevitable delay before health gain is identifiable. This presents a problem for a service with a tradition for very short-term accounting.

*Rationing Leads to the Development of New Ways of Providing Care*

The idea of 'your' family doctor, familiar with 'your' needs and problems, with an in depth understanding of 'your' environment is, some would insist, at the heart of good general practice. While the general concept and intention are excellent, resource limitation, increasing demand and the acquisition and application of secondary care skills by GPs and the rest of the team make it impossible to achieve.[4]

The traditional concept of the GP alone, rather than the team, as the first point of contact for patients has gone. GPs no longer just deal with minor problems referring everything serious to secondary care. It would be wrong to suggest that this is only a response to rationing. It reflects the growing maturity of primary care and the decreasing relevance of the barriers between primary and secondary care.

Personal continuity has been replaced with team continuity. The development of primary care nursing skills,[5] and with this the opportunity to provide an increasingly wide variety of skills in considerable depth close to the patient, is arguably a consequence of rationing and a benefit—a benefit which may be resisted at first by the consumer.

General practice is a traditional and conservative environment and there is usually active resistance to change. This is an attitude which has led to exasperation among some health professionals. They express the view that GP inertia and self centredness can hamper the development of health care. The welcome with which the end of fundholding was greeted lay only in part in the hope of the restoration of equality. It is also widely hoped that the change will allow greater integration across the traditional boundaries which, depending on your point of view, hedge or defend general practice. The power politics behind the formation of PCGs and their boards graphically illustrate this structural conservatism.

The establishment of GP and primary care nurse training, the elevation of the status of primary care and investment in infrastructure, has transformed what can be done in the GP's surgery. This has produced a dramatic impact upon mortality and morbidity. Nurse-led national initiatives in asthma and diabetes have lead to significant improvements. Initiatives in cardiovascular risk, cerebrovascular risk and chronic obstructive pulmonary disease will undoubtedly bring similar benefits. In our practice, a benign prostatic disease assessment programme is demonstrating that it is possible simultaneously to increase the quality of care and to reduce secondary care costs.

The juxtaposition of GPs and secondary care specialists in 'outreach clinics' within practices is stimulating new ways of looking at chronic disease management. In our practice tripartite discussions between an ophthalmologist, a GP and a local optician suggest that the opportunity to meet several quality issues, to apply evidence-based protocols and to improve proximity to the patient can be combined with the cost reduction of shared care.

## Rationing Stimulates the Development of New Skills

For the individual professional, with opportunities for training, the general shortage of resources can be a stimulus. A secretary can acquire strategic computing skills, nurses have learned phlebotomy, minor surgery techniques (N2 cautery), ENT skills, male catheterisation and the management of certain chronic diseases.

The list of acquired skills continues to grow. GPs can enjoy the satisfaction of developing skills acquired as hospital doctors in training or as clinical assistants and can explore the opportunities of complementary medicine. Although the spur in part is limited funds, the outcome is greater professional satisfaction, greater quality of medical care and greater availability and relevance for the consumer, as well as a reduction in cost. This increasing list of skills contributes to the quality and breadth of health care that each frontline health worker can offer. The inevitable inefficiency of referral is reduced. It is a process which needs to be developed and rewarded.

## Rationing Justifies Economy and the Ability to Say No!

Limited funds have forced everyone involved to question what is truly necessary and what is not. Are simple remedies for short-term ailments something the NHS should pay for or not? Should the NHS fund transport to hospital when patients with life-threatening health problems must wait for treatment? Is it appropriate to maintain this level of care? Pressure on resources forces a debate about what quality in health care means, which services continue to be necessary and which do not. The key questions are, which aspects of health care does the NHS need to guarantee, and which aspects should patients fund themselves? There is great reluctance to address these crucial issues.

The notion of PCGs directly accountable to the communities they serve could provide an opportunity for this debate. But this will only happen if PCGs take this responsibility seriously. This means very much more than relying on the single 'token' lay board member's voice. There is a real danger that as this degree of accountability is alien to the traditional, paternalistic, structural orientation of the NHS, it will be avoided.

## 2. The Obvious Problems of Limited Funds

Reading the preceding paragraphs one might be tempted to imagine that rationing has brought nothing but benefits and that therefore the provision of adequate funds is unnecessary! I should be very unpopular with my colleagues if this was interpreted as my view. The problem of resource shortage in the NHS has been and continues to be very damaging to the nation's health. Particularly damaging is the tradition of focus on short-term input costs rather than the assessment of the long-term gains in outcome as described elsewhere. There is evidence that this is beginning to change.

### *Problems For Patients*

*Financial Considerations of Health Care Are Not Well Understood by Patients*

The general public has been constantly reassured by successive governments that they are entitled to the very best health care—a message reinforced by the media. The discovery that there is a risk of dying while awaiting treatment or, at the other extreme, that an appointment to see your GP is not available for several days or weeks, understandably causes frustration, misunderstanding and the search for a scapegoat.

How can the NHS, which is free and supposedly 'the envy of the world', deny a proven life-saving drug, or a drug which may significantly improve quality of life, to anyone who needs it, whatever the expense? Why should patients used to having free chiropody or ready access to long-term residential care now have to pay?

The financial considerations, now an everyday part of general practice, are poorly understood by patients. They have been taught to expect lifelong, readily available, quality care. This situation is further aggravated for the GP by the seemingly universal practice of all who work in the NHS to resolve enquiries and complaints directed at them by referring the enquirer 'to their GP'.

No matter how reasonable and acceptable a decision may seem when applied to the service in general terms, the health problems of patients or members of their families remain the focus of their own world and, understandably, in their eyes deserve special treatment. Statistical reality and the logical restriction on care become meaningless when you or a close relative are the statistic.

## Waiting

Waiting lists are rationing in human form. Perhaps they are of little importance for the pain-free inguinal hernia, but waiting six months for a coronary artery bypass or angioplasty because medication is no longer controlling frequent episodes of angina requires considerable fortitude and even heroism. Sadly the most vociferous or influential may benefit over the most needy in these situations.

## Inconvenience

The present pressure on hospital resources not only makes care less available by creating waiting lists but also makes the provision of that care less flexible for the patient. For people in work or with other commitments there is little opportunity to plan for time off work or away from the home. Notice is usually short and peremptory. The opportunity to choose when to have an operation has been a potent selling feature of private health schemes.

## The Consequences of Delays in Treatment

General practitioners are very aware of the impact of long waiting lists on patients' lives and are frequently asked to provide 'please expedite' letters. Apart from the obvious anxiety and prolonged time out of work through treatable incapacity, there is undoubtedly an increase in chronic morbidity and the danger of the development of a chronic state of invalidity, which is either incurable or at least costly to reverse.

For anyone, the pain of an osteoarthritic hip has a marked effect on the quality of life, but in the most common sufferers, the elderly, it can cause an irreversible change in mobility. Even when surgery is at last offered, learned attitudes to their health, as a result of prolonged immobility and dependence, can have an adverse effect on the outcome.

'Social invalidity', occurring when there are long delays in treatment, may cause people who have been out of work for many months to find it impossible to get back to work at all. This has lasting financial consequences for both the patient and the state. Nor is it only the patient who suffers as a consequence of delay. The financial dependents and those who are dependent for care will also suffer. From the GP's perspective, the apparent short-term result of limited funds, the waiting list, has many hidden long-term costs. These should be taken into account.

It should be noted that 'systems thinking' suggests caution in the search for a quick solution to long, politically embarrassing waiting lists. A sudden injection of large amounts of money may over the longer term distort and even compound the problem by failing to address the 'process' issues involved.

A topical example is 'bed blocking' of acute hospital beds by the dependent elderly and the chronic sick. A narrow perception of savings in a social services budget can paradoxically prove extremely expensive when considered without the responsible barriers between local authorities and hospital trusts. The ultimate goal of combining health funds for communities served by individual PCGs may allow these illogicalities to be addressed.

## The Patient's Anxiety About the GP's Motivation

The average general practitioner appointment time of seven minutes is very short for the holistic care of several complex and interrelated problems. General practitioners have been slow to point out that their increasing responsibility for more complex care will take longer. Patients are aware that they are being rushed. They are vociferously aware that GPs are difficult to see and the concept of waiting lists, acceptable in hospital, is not in the GP surgery. Few management discussions in GPs' surgeries do not touch on patient demand and the appointment system.

Worse than this is the fact that patients are justifiably con-cerned about what is motivating their GP's choice. Is the GP actually deciding the most medically appropriate treatment, the most cost-effective or the cheapest? The development of protocols of care by national clinical governance bodies and the advice given by officers of the health authorities also come under similar suspicion. It continues to remain unclear if clinical governance or even cost-effectiveness is about quality or cost.

Decisions made according to current 'evidence-based protocols' are rarely clear cut.[6] The universal application of treatment for raised blood lipids poses a huge financial threat and is being questioned. The evidence for treatment of patients with clear risk of cardiovascular disease is proven and encouraged. However the research is mainly on patients under 70 years. Does this mean that 71- or 75-year-old patients are denied treatment? Common sense would suggest such a crude cut-off point is absurd.

The choice of medication is an easy and obvious target when financial resources are limited. In theory this can lead to the selection of drugs which may be adequate but of noticeably different quality. It is too easy to insist that the pressure to stay within a prescribing budget does not place pressure on the prescribing GP. This ignores the possibility that hospital services may have to be cut and staff made redundant as a consequence of overspending. Patients are justified in being suspicious of the prescribing habits of GPs under pressure to lower their prescribing costs.

## Problems for General Practitioners and other Primary Care Staff

### The Pressure of a Rising Workload

For the working GP these patient anxieties only add to the pressure already caused by the rising workload.[7] The nature of general practice is changing rapidly. To the stress of a rising workload is added the stress of a changing environment, changing opportunity and changing expectation. Other causes of stress are the increasing complexity of the GP's practice management, the technological changes and the demands of the superstructure, the health authority and the Department of Health. The formation of primary care groups could aggravate this unless the insights of new management thinking are applied.

It is easy for the GP to feel trapped in a boiling cauldron of activity into which new and unfamiliar ingredients are constantly being added.

It is not surprising therefore that, over the course of a long day, attention may be diverted away from the needs of the patient. The GP's ability to focus on the patient's holistic needs may be diminished. It is easy to miss the wider dimensions of a patient's health problems or even actively not to seek them. The story of the patient, for months attending his GP for his usual symptomatic treatment, who when inadvertently seen by another GP, a partner or a locum, is found to have a chronic, once treatable problem is not uncommon.

The antibiotic and the 'sick note' take two minutes to provide.[8] An explanation about the lack of effect of antibiotics in self-limiting viral illnesses and advice about simple home remedies and the ills of smoking take very much longer. This is particularly so when time has to be spent undoing long established misconceptions that antibiotics are a good thing because 'My last doctor always gave them to me when I had a cold'!

## Adversely Affected Relationships and Communication

Rationed NHS resources and the effect of this on manpower, coupled with rising demand, even from a stable population, forces GPs to ration time and effort with individual patients. This inevitably cuts into the ability to create the relationship which gives the patient permission to share the deeper concerns, causes and consequences of their health problems.

Good communication is 95 per cent focused listening. With a queue of patients, the GP running 30 minutes late needs great dedication to remain silent and to resist putting the 'closed' question.

## Limits To Professional Freedom

Rationing funds in primary care will affect the GP's choice of medication, while their restriction elsewhere in the service limits the GP's choice of secondary care, possibly to second best. A long delay in the availability of physiotherapy may deter appropriate referral. As has already been shown, this may lead to a long-term reduction in health.

*Reduction in Motivation and Morale in Primary Care*

With primary care staff conscious of the anxiety caused to patients and the stress caused by a lack of resources, it is not surprising that morale is low and recruitment falling.[9] In general practice, the growing demand for posts, for which at least the time commitment is finite and the managerial and financial responsibility minimal, is another symptom of the problem. There is diminishing enthusiasm for the traditional full-time commitment to the health of a community from the 'full partner', particularly where demography suggests a high level of demand.

The tragedy for any ethical profession, such as nursing or medicine, is that its members may feel trapped by the knowledge that their actions impact directly upon the innocent. This knowledge means that the only justifiable form of protest left to the professionals is to leave, taking with them valuable skills and costly expertise.

The effect of rationing health care, from the perspective of general practice, without a concurrent rationing of demand, is a threat to quality. This creates a vicious spiral of increasing stress, decaying morale and rising secondary expense, caused by those taking the easy option of referral or unnecessary prescription. This in turn adds to the drain on health resources.

Investment in NHS staff and on improving morale will always be more than repaid. This is not a simple matter of levels of remuneration, but of respect for the individual, the creation of opportunities for self actualisation and imaginative empowerment.

## 3. The Weaknesses of the Current System Which Rationing Aggravates

*A Lack of Consumer Responsibility*

The original and laudable concept of health care, free at the point of delivery, which underpinned the formation of the NHS in 1948 has been very effective in reducing the patient's financial anxieties. Regrettably with this reduction in anxiety there has been a reduction in the consciousness of the value or worth of what is demanded. More troubling still, responsibility either to use the service appropriately or first to attempt simple personal health remedies is eroded. Many patients consider it an obvious 'right' to have the health care they demand.

The conscious effort to reduce the risks and liabilities of the sick and needy has created an inevitable mismatch between patient expectation and what it is possible to provide with limited resources. This not only causes frustration but presents a threat to the system itself. The action of the patient who calls the GP at 2.00 a.m. because they have a sore throat, or their oral contraceptive pill has run out, can be irritating for the professionals who must deal with it. The true impact is the financial cost of the night visit and the consequent reduction in what may be spent on more vital services.

Why should any patient over 60 years ever purchase a paracetamol? It is a credit to the general public that requests for prescriptions for medication which can be purchased, such as paracetamol or cough remedies, are uncommon. The system certainly encourages it and protects those who abuse it. At a more subconscious level, paradoxically, as the quality of health care increases and accurate information on health becomes more available, rising appropriate demand will inevitably be accompanied by rising inappropriate demand, and, with it, dependency.

Of all the drugs prescribed, 'the GP' is the most addictive. Increasing dependency is becoming a worrying trend. On entering general practice I asked the senior partner how I could provide a caring available service without making the patient dependent. He did not know and, a number of years later, neither do I. Easy comments about patient education demonstrate the ignorance of the commentator, no more.

### The Dependence on Short-term Measurements of Resource Input

A major flaw in the current system, which has distorted strategic planning of health care provision, has been the almost exclusive focus on measurement of financial input and with it pressure to reduce costs, often over the very short term.

Our practice, seeking to improve the quality of asthma care, was for several years criticised for our higher than average use of inhaled bronchodilators and inhaled steroids. Considered solely in terms of input, this was an above average expense. However, when outcomes were measured for the first time, in this case hospital admissions for acute respiratory problems, they were found to be very substantially less than the average of the ten neighbouring practices.

Savings to the budgets of the local hospital must have been great, although never reflected in the practice prescribing budget, and must have hugely outweighed any additional medication costs. It will take considerable vision to recognise the escalation in the general practice prescribing costs in lipid lowering therapy as an investment to reduce the costs of coronary and stroke care in the future. To complicate the picture further, the outcome of longevity and its social consequences have to be remembered.

Great sensitivity and vision is needed in leading and monitoring general practice development to ensure that imaginative and innovative ideas are not stifled because they appear costly when considered over the short term. The consequence of demotivating a responsible innovator is always costly and this must be recognised in funding decisions. The Audit Commission was brave to dismiss fundholding as costly and uneconomic after an experiment lasting less than five years!

## Is Big Always Best?

The danger of universal equality, that bland adherence to the dogma of widespread conformity, can seriously threaten issues of local relevance and local creativity. Identification with a socially or geographically distinct community can be a powerful motivation for local innovation and for the joint involvement of both statutory and voluntary organisations in developing care. Identification with such communities should not be sacrificed for assumed benefits of scale.

The massive, centrally directed bureaucracy of the NHS creates a very narrow business methodology and culture. Management demands can damage good progress with a tangle of complexity. The short-lived experiment of fundholding began to address the issues of peripheral empowerment and responsibility. Centrally directed rationing can prevent local initiative and the development of local experiments in rationalisation. This situation is further complicated by the involvement of several different responsible agencies.

The so-called economies of scale can turn out to be 'absurdity in conformity' when considered at the individual general practice or peripheral health care interface. Primary care groups will have to decide consciously whether to give greater priority to central direction or to cultivate a productive dialogue with their local communities.

## Health Care is Too Compartmentalised

Having identified a weakness of the current system as being too centrally directed and sacrificing local relevance for consistency, it might appear illogical to suggest that health care within the NHS has become too compartmentalised. But inter-discipline and department boundaries are strenuously protected, particularly when resources are limited. The lack of leadership and the almost total absence of a shared vision in the NHS, despite cries of 'patient-centred, quality-driven, free at the point of need, primary-care led' has meant that considerable time, effort and funds are used in defending territory and administrative boundaries.

There is a need to reshape thinking about health care in a wider arena at community or neighbourhood level and to consider issues of transparency. It is the development of a shared community vision of health by those who can not only influence change, but will also suffer or benefit from their decisions within an identifiable geographical or social entity, that will force a rational restructuring of health agencies.

The natural inter-relatedness of community[10] could be the most powerful motivator for change in health provision. General practice is ideally placed to provide that leadership. The 1997 white paper could represent an opportunity for this to happen,[11] but the identification of populations of 100,000 to 150,000 as 'preferred' for the new primary health care groups seems more like administrative convenience than sensitivity to the natural forces of community. It remains to be seen whether PCGs will accept the challenge.

## 4. Rationing is Acceptable Provided Certain Conditions Are Met

Rationing health care is a concept which everyone can accept. Everyone is familiar with the process of decision-making undertaken in every shop and supermarket—'What do I want? What do I need? What can I afford?' However to make this acceptable in health care certain conditions, which are not common, need to be met.

*Accurate Benchmarks Are Essential*

An obvious necessity is the accurate and visible identification of relative need and transparent, statistically based benchmarks to determine how funds are distributed. The problems experienced in defining accurate benchmarks to predict levels of prescribing by the Prescription Pricing Authority (PPA) indicate the difficulty. It was only in 1988 that the concept of prescribing units (PUs) was introduced. This determined that patients over 65 years (three PUs) were likely to require three times the drug costs of patients under 65 years (one PU).

This was the first time that the possibility that patients over 65 years might require on average more medication than those under 65 years had been statistically recognised. Even here the multiplier three was selected 'because it seemed a good number' (personal communication). Since then the PPA has introduced ASTRO-PUs (age, sex and temporary resident adjusted)[12] and more recently STAR (Specific Therapeutic Group Age Sex Related Prescribing Units) which takes some account of the special additional costs of chronic disease.

Compared with this, the GP's capitation payment is calculated in three age bands 0-65, 65-75 and over 75 years.[13] The ratios between the amounts allocated to each age band is loosely based on a household survey in 1990. Recent workload studies suggest this benchmark system is much less accurate than the decision by the PPA to use a multiplier of three for patients over 65 years in 1988.

This means that general practitioners looking after very elderly or very young populations are working very much harder and longer hours than average for up to 20 per cent less income. It also means that, when demand is considered, the elderly have less invested in their GPs than the rest of the population. Without the use of accurate benchmarks[14] bizarre distortions of funding occur and large sections of the population are disadvantaged.

## Choices Should Be Shared

That the unavoidable choices implicit within rationing should be made as close to the consumer as possible is a personal and strongly held view. The often quoted disadvantage of the possibility of inequality in health provision is, in my opinion, outweighed by the opportunity to modify services according to local choices about quality and relevance.

Accountability both to the local population served and to a local vision of health is a vital consideration. It also presents an opportunity to stimulate co-operation between statutory and voluntary organisations, to reduce abuse and wastage of a service which is locally owned and to allow new ideas for health improvement to develop beyond the narrow confines and boundaries of general practice.

## A Shared Vision and Leadership Is Needed

However acceptable rationing is, the development of a shared vision, not just the presentation of political platitudes, is essential. The unreliability of such platitudes ensures that they are now greeted with disbelieving cynicism. A shared vision of health care means creating an absolute commitment, which has been 'bought into' by all concerned, especially the taxpayer. Accurate costing and open discussion about the implementation as well as the unavoidable consequences of rationing can restore confidence.

For consumers to become involved, concerned and responsible for the use of limited funds, choices have to be made, wherever possible, close to those who will experience their effects. This needs peripheral as well as central leadership charged with the identification and constant modification of a truly shared vision of health care—a shared vision based on the honest assessment of needs and the realities of limited funds.

The issues of scale and ownership are extremely important in the creation of a shared vision. As I have suggested before, the best place for this to occur is within a natural community. The concept of a 'learning organisation'[15] currently gaining credibility may have particular relevance to the development of primary care in this context. Much of the necessary structure already exists. It is to be hoped that the focus on the consumer will create new opportunities for a broader understanding of health gain and community development, albeit within the confines of limited resources. This focus is a central concept of a 'learning organisation'

## 5. Reconciling Rationing with the Maintenance of Quality

### Providing a Spur for Innovation

As has been argued, rationing can be a spur to create new ideas for service development. Health care is astonishingly fortunate, relative to many other industries, because each individual member of the workforce has already demonstrated an inclination to be involved in serving the sick and co-operating in improving health care. Personal dedication and commitment is a far more powerful motivator than financial gain. The caring services are blessed with a high level of dedicated activity, which is neither recognised nor rewarded.

It is a matter of concern that the NHS, an organisation that has the object of providing holistic concerned care for patients, has such a poor record for the care and the morale of its workforce.

This power source needs to be tapped and properly recognised through the creation of a clear shared vision in which both consumer and worker contribute and benefit. The identification and support of leaders and 'change agents', wherever they may appear particularly close to the patient, needs to be encouraged and rewarded by greater empowerment.

### Creating Teams and Leaders

At the 'work face' such empowerment[16] allows the development of focused teams able to co-ordinate care or better still ignore traditional barriers. For example the barriers between primary and secondary care, between general practice and social services, between general practice and local authorities and between general practice and community trusts.

The use of 'continuous quality improvement' tools and techniques could facilitate this process.[17] Remarkably, even for nurses from different disciplines, practice nurses, community nurses, health visitors, and midwives caring for the same community, opportunities to meet regularly are uncommon. The idea of nurses as a group making decisions about their work and the rationalisation of care is revolutionary and where it occurs has taken time and considerable determination to achieve.

If nurses find team co-ordination and personal direction and empowerment difficult to achieve, the equally necessary co-ordination of voluntary organisations, local authority, social services and primary care toward a shared vision of community health can seem impossible.

## Developing Skills and Challenging Barriers

With technological advance and the development of new therapies, more can be offered in general practice. Imaginative general practice at present represents the most cost-effective method of providing health care.[18] It is essential that, even from the limited funds available, resources must be focused on training and developing new skills in all who work in primary care. Space and time must be set aside for training and genuine cost-effective innovation.

Movement of work must be accompanied by the movement of appropriate funds. There is a new housing development nearby on land recently occupied by hospital wards. The health authority has suggested that the closure of these wards and the return of patients to their homes and local nursing and rest homes has had no impact whatever on the local primary care workload. Such an assertion has a powerful demotivating effect on local GPs, whose experience suggests otherwise.

There must be a clear channel for the savings made on hospital services in primary care to be reinvested in primary care. This is particularly important at a time of financial restraint as there will then be huge pressure simply to use savings to balance hospital budgets.

It has been shown elsewhere that threatening the quality of care in trying to achieve short-term saving can prove costly in the longer term both financially and in its social consequences. Great courage will be required to recognise, reward and encourage quality innovations in which savings are only realisable in the longer term. Paradoxically, when resources are limited, concern for quality and the rapid, effective and relevant provision of health care becomes more not less essential. Short-term saving can ultimately prove the more costly option.

Equally essential, the traditional hierarchy of authority with its innumerable divisions and barriers, often of only historic significance, must submit to imaginative local-community-driven re-engineering. Just as medical diagnostic techniques and therapies are constantly changing, so too must the system that delivers this care constantly change. Sensitivity to the needs and opportunities of the community served remains essential. Central management must diminish to provide only visionary leadership and the fair administration of the rules and limits that encompass the service.

## Increasing Patient Involvement

In the context of the realities of rationing the involvement of patients is, in my opinion, of crucial importance. Elsewhere consumer ownership and the motivating effect of empowering the community have been identified. At individual practice level the involvement of patients in strategy development and in the difficult choices posed by rationing remain elusive and uncommon.

The issue of accountability to the taxpaying public and to the patient population represented is of crucial importance. Lines of accountability must be explicit and democratic. Patient participation groups (PPGs) could provide a valuable link between health care providers and the community. PPG members have been given the opportunity to learn about the complex structure and relationships that those who work in the NHS or other health care organisations take for granted, but which mystify the general public.

PPGs that are to be durable need the motivation of effectiveness and influence to continue to give time to the effort. Focus groups and public meetings are poor alternatives, lacking the breadth and depth of understanding to offer more than personal opinions. The frequently abysmal attendance at such community information meetings proves the complexity of this issue.

The traditional general practice culture of the senior partner-led hierarchy remains a block to the effectiveness of even the best informed PPG's voice and will ultimately lead to their demotivation. Where a practice has had the courage to develop a team culture and to empower the individual teams within their areas of responsibility it becomes easier, although never easy, to establish and integrate a patient participation group. There is real anxiety that primary care groups with their very limited lay representation could paradoxically reduce the effectiveness and motivation of individual practice PPGs.

## 6. Finally

Rationing in health care has both damaging and beneficial effects. It is inevitable and must be planned for. Concealing and excluding the consumer from the reality of limited resources creates a mismatch between expectation and what is actually possible. Peripheral empowerment and widespread leadership, which cut across the traditional concepts of central control, could create the necessary climate for the development of new ideas which rationalise care, are cost effective and yet retain a high level of quality.

Responsibility for the consequences of the decisions made in the ballot box should, as far as possible, rest with the voter. It is for leaders within health care to identify the necessary choices and to encourage the development of clinical understanding to ensure that the debate is well informed. This way the outcome will be clearly understood and widely owned.

General practitioners and the primary health care team are at the interface between the public and the health care services. For this reason they will always be particularly sensitive to the realities of rationing.

# Rationing: An Inappropriate Response To A Real Problem

## Harry Burns

Rationing of health care is inevitable. Important people say so—frequently. It seems that the free health care provided by the NHS is so desirable that queues of otherwise healthy people are lining up outside health centres and hospitals demanding free operations. They aren't? Well, the absence of hordes of the worried well demanding treatment must be due to waiting lists—which are a form of rationing. We all know that if there were no waiting lists, the queues would soon form. The population of Britain has a bottomless pit of health care needs and we can never afford to meet those needs. We should throw in the towel and admit it now. Furthermore, we should be up-front and explicit about it all. Explicit rationing, it is said, is 'vital for the moral management of health care'.[1]

The question of rationing of care and its inevitability provoke strongly held opinions. The Rationing Agenda Group lines up against the forces of the Anti-Rationing Group. Academics are prominent in both camps. Clinicians, who are responsible for implementing rationing policies and who are, each day, face to face with the patients affected by them, view the debate with wry amusement. They remark on how often the protagonists in the debate are philosophers, economists or policy analysts and how infrequently those at the sharp end of health care become involved. Most just want to treat patients. In fact, practising clinicians, every day of their professional lives, make more or less rational judgments about the use of resources available to them. They usually do so implicitly and, by applying clinical wisdom in a sensible fashion, they contribute greatly to making the NHS one of the most efficient health care systems in the world. Furthermore, they would tell the theorists that there is a strong argument that harm is done to patients by making decisions explicit.[2] Many would point to the risk that, by accepting explicit rationing as inevitable, considerable damage may be done to the NHS. In examining the two commonly held views that (a) rationing is inevitable and (b) the basis of rationing decisions should be explicit, I do so from the viewpoint of someone who spent 15 years treating patients as a hospital clinician and who, for the past nine years, has participated in the purchasing and commissioning processes which have developed in the NHS.

### *Rationing Is Inevitable*

The basis for this statement is that there is an unlimited demand for health care in the population. This seems an untested assumption and supporting empirical evidence is not easy to find. Donald Light has pointed to the fact that, in rather better funded systems such as Holland and Germany, there are no waiting lists for treatment and no evidence of unlimited demand for care.[3] There is admittedly evidence that, left to make the judgement for themselves, patients will tend to consume health care at a higher rate than health professionals would advise. However, we are not dealing with a system in which patients' access to health care is based on demand. The NHS sets out to make health care free to patients at the time of *need*. It has never sought to meet demand and refusing to meet demands for services from which a patient will not benefit cannot be construed as rationing.

If there is no convincing evidence of a bottomless pit of demand, there is certainly no evidence of unlimited need, and the basis for rationing becomes an economic one. It may be that the costs of care are rising at a rate which is beyond the ability of Western economies to sustain. There is some truth in this. David Eddy[4] has calculated that health care costs are increasing about twice as fast as general price inflation. There are two main reasons for this. Firstly, medical inflation, the rate of increase in the cost of clinical equipment, drugs and clinical salaries, is greater that routine price inflation, the rate of increasing costs of day-to-day commodities. Secondly, clinical innovation is leading to greater intensity of service. Twenty years ago, little might be done for patients with advanced cancer or degenerative neurological disease. Nowadays ever more expensive drugs and interventions are improving prognosis, and so the pressure mounts to intervene more.

It seems that this difference between the rate of growth in health care costs and the rate of growth of Western economies is a real tension which might justify demands for rationing. Yet, if the problem is one of macro-economics, why do we immediately assume that the only available answer is denial of needed care to individual patients? Perhaps a more appropriate response to the mantra: 'rationing is inevitable', is to say 'only if the electorate votes into power a government which is not prepared to spend sufficient money on health to allow needs to be met'. Governments have to make choices between greater or less public spending, between expenditure on roads, social services, defence, industrial developments, health. It is entirely legitimate for them to increase or decrease the proportion of public funds spent on health. If they fail to increase expenditure at an appropriate rate, some patients will be denied access to necessary care and rationing will be a reality. The decision is that of a democratically elected government which is accountable to the electorate. As a voter, I may be undecided about whether or not I want my taxes to increase to pay for new health care facilities but it would be nice to be asked rather than have a group of academics decide for me that I do not.

The problem with well-meaning academics arguing passionately that rationing is inevitable is that it denies the electorate—and patients—the possibility that their elected representatives might respond to unmet need by increasing the amount of public money spent on meeting that need. A government caught in the dilemma of lowering or raising taxes will usually be grateful for acceptance of the principle of rationing, for it means that health care demands become one less issue for them to worry about in the Public Expenditure Survey. If we conclude from the start that we can never adequately meet all needs, why bother trying to meet them as inadequately as we do already? Why not cut the NHS budget by 10 per cent or 20 per cent?[5] Inevitably, rationing becomes a self-fulfilling prophecy which ultimately destroys the fundamental principles of the NHS. Some might argue that such radical change would be no bad thing. The system of care that was right for 1948 may not be the most effective system for the twenty-first century. That is a separate debate which we cannot have until we have established that the electorate is unwilling to bear the extra costs of meeting unmet need. However, opinion polls suggest that most people are willing to pay more in taxes for better health care.

### Rationing Is With Us Now

Undeniably, rationing is a fact of life in the NHS. Hospitals are staffed at levels which make it difficult to spend enough time with patients. Waiting lists to be seen at clinics, to be investigated and to be treated, ration resources in a clumsy but effective manner. The state of crumbling Victorian institutions demonstrates rationing of capital. The unavailability of major items of medical equipment, taken for granted elsewhere, can lead to patients suffering harm or even dying as a result of rationing. Cases in which patients are transported hundreds of miles in an ambulance in search of an intensive care bed, or a staffed MRI scanner, rightly cause concern. One could hardly ask for more explicitness in rationing than that a dying boy should bypass a hospital because its X-ray department is closed after 6.00 p.m. to save overtime payments to radiographers. Where is the logic in responding to such situations with meek acceptance? Other responses are possible. Arguments for improving the funding of health care in this country can be made, yet proponents of rationing seem unable to countenance them.

New, in an article supporting the proposition that rationing is inevitable and should be explicit, identified four ways in which the funding gap in health care might be bridged.

1.  Improve efficiency of existing services

2.  Stop offering clinically ineffective services

3.  Redeploy resources from other areas of public expenditure

4.  Raise taxes

While admitting that these strategies would be successful in easing resource constraints, the argument he then advances to discount them seems to be that decisions would need to be made on how the newly found resource would be deployed:

During this deployment process, however, the health care system would be faced with deciding which of those beneficial services that it had previously chosen not to offer, now to offer (and to whom). This also requires a decision on which services still not to offer (yet). Hence providing more resources still requires the fundamental issues to be faced.[6]

Which fundamental issues? That rationing is inevitable? This argument offers no insight into that question. One can argue about the extent to which improved clinical efficiency or effectiveness might bridge the funding shortfall or how much tax might have to go up and how unacceptable that rise might be, but it seems clear that the main argument in support of the proposition that rationing is inevitable is because its proponents say so.

Different forms of rationing exist at present. Their existence is merely a demonstration that existing resources are inadequate or inadequately applied to the problems in the NHS. Their existence does not mean that rationing will exist indefinitely or that it will worsen. Existing forms of rationing will disappear if the electorate has the will to pay the price. This is the debate we should be having. Hand wringing Jeremiahs pointing to waiting lists and proclaiming that the end of the NHS-world is at hand add little to that debate.

### Decision-Making on Resource Use Should Be Explicit

Although it has been argued that rationing is not inevitable, until there is a political will to provide adequate resources, the types of rationing already mentioned—rationing by dilution, as Klein has described it[7]—will continue as a daily reality for clinicians. Should they continue to make rationing decisions implicitly and on a case-by-case basis or should there be a nationally agreed set of rules indicating what should or should not be provided by the NHS?

On the face of it, the present system by which health authorities determine local priorities has produced disturbing anomalies. Access to infertility care, treatments for Alzheimers, motor neurone disease, multiple sclerosis and some treatments for cancer, can be determined by the area one lives in. The public are confused and disturbed by postcode medicine and the explicit rationing lobby see explicitness of decision-making as an appropriate response. Health authorities limiting access to these treatments can make their decisions very explicit. They might, with some justification, claim that infertility is not an illness so the NHS is under no obligation to treat it. They might argue that the evidence for benefit of some of the drugs licensed to treat neurological disease is far from conclusive and the cost-effectiveness of some of the newer anti-cancer drugs is far from clear. Is that explicit enough? Does that explanation make an infertile couple or a patient with cancer feel any better? Mooney and Lange[8] have argued not. They have described the notion of deprivation disutility. Patients suffering from an incurable illness experience a measurable decrease in health. That decrease in health, or disutility, is greater if they are also informed that a cure for their condition is available but that there is insufficient money to purchase it. So who benefits from explicitness? Surely explicitness serves mainly to benefit the doctor who can shrug his shoulders and pass the responsibility for rationing onto faceless bureaucrats who can pass the blame onto governmental parsimony. Mooney and Lange[9] argue persuasively that the one person who clearly does not benefit is the patient.

Another powerful argument against an explicit rule-based rationing system is the fact that patients are different.[10] A statement that 'insertion of grommets into the ears of children with chronic otitis media is ineffective' may be broadly true at a population level but does not exclude the possibility that an individual case in certain circumstances might benefit from the procedure. Attempts to protocolise and define clinical care can deny needed treatment to an individual. It denies the existence of art in clinical practice. That art is to be found in treating a patient as a unique individual and finding the best pattern of care for him. Furthermore, explicit rule-setting is probably unenforceable.[11] Clinicians can always bend the rules in individual cases by redefining the problem. Who would argue with a clinician's determination that a given procedure was necessary except another clinician? To make the explicit rationing system work, a whole new bureaucracy designed to provide second opinions would be necessary. Such a system would be a waste of resources, compounding the problem it was set up to resolve.

### *If Explicit Rationing Is Essential, Someone Must Be Doing It*

An important part of any argument in support of explicit rationing is that there should be a reasonable prospect of achieving a workable rationing system. To date, few health care systems attempting to ration explicitly seem to have had much success. Hunter has pointed to the political difficulties in Britain of introducing a system of rationing.[12] He even argues that it would be almost impossible to involve politicians in an effective debate on the topic. Other countries have gone past the stage of debate and attempted to introduce systems for limiting access to care. Sweden, for example, has defined a series of priorities for its health care system. These are:

1a. Treatment of life-threatening conditions or of diseases which, if left untreated, will lead to permanent disability or premature death

1b. Treatment of severe chronic diseases. Palliative terminal care and care of people with reduced autonomy

2. Individualised prevention and rehabilitation services

3. Treatment of less severe acute and chronic disease

4. Borderline cases

5. Care for reasons other than disease or injury

This list appears in a document which took three years to produce.[13] Most clinicians in Britain will view this time scale with astonishment. I doubt if there is a doctor anywhere in Britain who runs his clinical practice according to any other set of priorities and who could not have written this list, in exactly the same order, with about five minutes thought. The astonishing thing is not the list but the fact that someone thought it necessary to write it down.

Holland went through a similar process culminating in a report which attempted to restrict provision of services. This attempt has been radically modified in the light of public opposition. A report published in 1997 concluded that '... there is little political support for removing access to specific services from collective responsibility'.[14] The Dutch experience supports Hunter's view that the explicit rationing is too difficult for politicians to tackle.[15]

An interesting development has occurred in Oregon. It seems that some conditions which were 'below the line' for funding originally are progressing to the point where complications are developing which entitle the patient to treatment. This is an observation that will have public health specialists groaning in frustration. Guidelines are now being developed to allow provision of services to these patients. This may not have been the most cost-effective way of dealing with those patients! The original list of approved treatments is being expanded in a number of other areas.[16]

There are other examples where, under the guise of 'equity' or fiscal prudence, bureaucracies are being set up to determine what patients can receive as health care. As yet, there is little evidence to suggest that these systems are any better than the implicit decisions clinicians make about priorities every time they see a patient.

### The Future

The debate on explicit or implicit rationing is sterile until we know that the public is unwilling to pay for needs to be met. In settling that question it would be useful to commission work on future scenarios for health care in this country. Realistic assessment of what we might be required to provide even five years in the future would be useful.

# Rationing Cancer Care

# Karol Sikora

## Introduction

Rationing has been an integral part of health care since medicine began. So why has it so suddenly become such a hot topic? The technological scope of what we can do today surpasses the treatments of even 25 years ago. With it has come costs for staff, equipment and facilities in a world that is increasingly aware of the relationship between cost and product. There has been a major shift in the relationship between those involved in delivering health services and those involved in paying for them. Value judgements have to be made of the relative merits of certain interventions. Are they worth it for a particular individual? The eternal triangle of patient, doctor and payer is illustrated in Figure 1. We have seen the strong line between patient and doctor gradually erode with the doctor forging far stronger links to the payer. This is a common feature of all health care delivery systems. From Britain's National Health Service, through the social insurance plans of Germany to the emerging private insurance schemes of the former socialist countries and to the Health Maintenance Organisations in the US, individual patients are losing power. This chapter uses cancer treatment as an example of rationing in practice.

*Figure 1: The Doctor Patient Relationship*

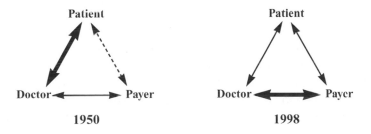

123

## Cancer and its Treatment

Successful radical surgery with curative intent for common cancer first took place over a hundred years ago. Radiotherapy followed as a second radical treatment for localised cancer in certain parts of the body and as an effective palliative measure in other situations. Chemotherapy, discovered by the US military through chemical warfare research, can cure certain rare cancers and prolong survival in many. The global incidence of cancer is soaring due to rapidly ageing populations in most countries. By the year 2020, there will be 20 million new cancer patients each year.[1] Seventy per cent of them will live in countries that between them will have less than five per cent of the treatment resources. We have seen an explosion in our understanding of the disease at a molecular level and are now poised to see some very significant advances in the clinic. Dramatic technological change is likely in surgery, radiotherapy and chemotherapy leading to increased cure rates, but at a price. The completion of the human genome project will almost certainly bring sophisticated genetic risk assessment methods requiring careful integration into existing screening programmes. Preventive strategies could considerably reduce the global disease burden at low cost. And palliative care to relieve pain and suffering should be a basic right of all cancer patients. Cancer care is now poised to rapidly exploit scientific advances in a remarkable way.

There are several forces at work leading to major changes in payment structures for cancer care. Firstly the number of new cancer patients each year is increasing as the population ages. Seventy per cent of all cancer presents in the over-60's. Over the next 25 years there are no less than 31 countries which will see a 100 per cent increase in their over-60 population. Secondly treatment costs are escalating way beyond inflation. A standard radiotherapy machine in 1960 cost £80,000. Now the latest linear accelerator with the necessary multileaf collimator costs nearly £2 million. The number of staff required to operate such equipment has risen dramatically, further pushing up costs. New drugs have been introduced for breast and ovarian cancer which can cost over £6,000 per course. Unfortunately these drugs are only partially effective. Aggressive and sophisticated marketing strategies stimulate the demand needed if the pharmaceutical industry is to recoup its research and development costs.

Public expectation and media interpretation of cancer break-throughs fuelled by exciting press releases from the cancer charities suggest to many that cure may be possible. And political short-term expediency may see the use of relatively small funding bursts for cancer treatment to gain credence with electorates. After the recent election in the UK, the Labour government pledged £10 million for improving breast cancer services. However, this was to be used to set up 'one-stop' clinics for women with breast symptoms. As only one in ten have cancer the actual increase in funding was of the order of £35 per person—hardly the major development heralded by the government's spin doctors. In Holland last year, public disquiet led to the government agreeing to increase the health care budget by $12 million to buy adequate supplies of taxol to treat breast and ovarian cancer patients. The forces for change currently operating are:

- ageing population
- technological improvement and cost
- public expectation
- short term politics
- litigation
- drug company pricing
- media interpretation
- increased transparency
- increased frankness about cancer

## Assessing Cancer Care

Assessing the quality of cancer care is notoriously difficult. Clearly the most objective measurement is cure rate achieved for a given cancer type. Large groups of patients need to be amassed to make this comparison meaningful as there are many permuta-tions of the type of primary cancer, the pathological features (tumour grade) and the relative spread of the tumour in the body (tumour stage). Effective comparisons between hospitals are only possible for relatively common tumours. Cure rates, expressed as a five-year percentage survival, are known to show significant international variation, with the UK being low in the league table. Figures produced in 1998 by the Imperial Cancer Research Fund and the UK Office of National Statistics provide a fascinating glimpse of the British situation. The survival rate overall has risen from 25 per cent to 30 per cent since 1980 but is still poorer than the US average of nearly 40 per cent. The improvements have come in diseases such as breast cancer, colorectal cancer and non-Hodgkin's lymphoma. In lung, prostate, pancreas and oeso-phageal cancer there has been no improvement. Interestingly it is the diseases where improvement in survival has been achieved that show the poorest comparison to European statistics. The explanation is almost certainly the patchy availability of cancer care in the UK. The implementation of proposals to restructure cancer services and to provide an integrated hub-and-spoke structure with cancer centres and cancer units will hopefully ensure equity in this complex area.[2]

### *The Financial Bottom Line*

There are considerable international differences between the amount available for cancer treatment in countries of similar economic background (Table 1). The total size of the health care cake is clearly the financial starting point. This can go up by increasing taxation, reducing other public spending —defence is a good target in an increasingly peaceful world—or by seeking co-payments whereby patients pay small sums for various com-ponents of care: prescription charges, outpatient visits and hospital bed costs. Health care reforms may seek to address either the supply of or the demand for services. Supply-side rationing reduces beds, availability of chemotherapy daycare, creates a waiting list for radiotherapy treatment and the number of specialists available. Encouraging private practice or seeking co-payment attempts to reduce demand.

Whatever the financial bottom line, those involved in provision of services will inevitably seek improvements and ask for more. Where best to place additional resources is a matter of consider-able debate. There is clearly a limit to the health gain that can be obtained at any time because of technological limitations. Just increasing resources for the treatment of patients with metastatic lung cancer would be wasteful as there are at present no effective treatments other than palliation. In the private sector, competition limits wasteful development, so the number of fast food outlets in a particular town is limited by what the market will bear. This changes with time, demographics and taste. In the public sector there may appear to be no limits for the number of linear accelerators in London, for example. But expanding one part of the NHS means the contraction of another. The Calman Report on cancer services[3] has led to far-reaching changes in the UK for cancer patients, almost certainly at the expense of those with cardiovascular disease, diabetes and chronic problems of old age. I would argue, of course, that this is quite justifiable as cancer services in Britain have received little attention for the last 30 years.

### Table 1
### European Health Care Spend Indicators (WHO, 1995)

| Country | % of GDP[1] | Expenditure per person | |
|---|---|---|---|
| | | Health Care[2] | Drugs[3] |
| Great Britain | 6.9 | 1211 | 173 |
| Switzerland | 9.6 | 2294 | 404 |
| Germany | 9.5 | 1861 | 426 |
| France | 9.7 | 1866 | 358 |
| Netherlands | 8.8 | 1641 | 193 |
| Greece | 5.2 | 598 | 98 |

*Notes*:
1 Percentage of gross domestic product spent on health care
2 Spending per person in US$ at purchasing power parity
3 total drug spend per person in US$ at purchasing power parity

*Source*: Data on file, WHO, Geneva

## Prioritisation

Prioritisation is the key to rationing in practice. The problem is the reconciliation of different value judgements for specific interventions. Does, for example, a woman who says she is desperate to survive breast cancer deserve more courses of expensive chemotherapy than a patient who expresses no such feelings? Most healthcare professionals would say no. But then what about the relative merit of a mother with two small children compared with a single woman? And what about a woman who has attempted suicide twice and is a regular heroin taker with a long criminal record? We draw the line at this type of prioritisation in public but it is actually taking place.

### *An Example of Prioritising Cancer Chemotherapy*

- 12-year-old boy—stage IV Hodgkin's Disease. Requires ABVD chemotherapy and close follow up

- 42-year-old woman with stage II breast cancer. Requires adjuvant chemotherapy with CMF

- 35-year-old woman with stage III ovarian cancer. Requires Paclitaxel

- 63-year-old woman with metastatic breast cancer failed first line chemotherapy. Requires Docetaxel

- 60-year-old man with severe ischaemic heart disease. Liver metastases from colorectal cancer failed 5 Fluorouracil chemotherapy. Requires Irinotecan

- 74-year-old heavy smoker with metastatic lung cancer. For Gemcitabine

The six short clinical synopses in this list each cost about £5,000 to deal with. I have put them in priority order for the following reasons. The boy with Hodgkin's Disease would have a 90 per cent chance of cure with chemotherapy and a long period of good quality life ahead. The woman needing adjuvant chemotherapy for breast cancer will increase her chances of cure by 15 per cent and again have good quality life to follow. The 35-year-old woman with ovarian cancer is young and, although Paclitaxel chemotherapy may only prolong her life by two years, on average this may be very worthwhile. The three remaining examples show the difficulty when only partially effective treatments are available. Docetaxel prolongs survival by about six months in breast cancer. Is this worth £5,000? High cost salvage chemotherapy for colorectal cancer with Irinotecan is possible but the chances of it working are less than 15 per cent. Finally, why offer the heavy smoker an expensive drug when he will inevitably die of his disease rapidly? Whilst the extremes of this prioritisation exercise are clear the middle ground is blurred. This leads to different conclusions being reached by different groups of purchasers and thus, inevitably, 'postcode prescribing'. A major problem, of course, is that the patient can decide to go to the top of the pile simply by paying for the drugs themselves. This is becoming an increasingly common scenario in NHS cancer care.

### *Quality in Care Provision*

Determining priorities for chemotherapy use in this way can be carried out by doctors, multi-disciplinary conferences, citizens' juries or by using pre-set guidelines and is relatively straightforward. Allocating resources within the larger sphere of cancer care is far more complex. An ideal cancer treatment centre should be patient-friendly with welcoming reception staff, beverage services, and an architecturally sympathetic environment giving an atmosphere of hope. Complementary therapies, counselling and as much information as the patient and their carers want should be readily on hand. There should be no significant delays and, if necessary, interpreter services should be available. Fast-tracking of investigations and, if possible, same day planning—whereby a patient with cancer symptoms is sorted out in one day ending with a definitive treatment plan—should be possible for certain categories of problem such as breast lumps, haematuria or rectal bleeding. But this all costs money. How does the provision of a counselling service used by 400 patients in one year compare with the drug costs involved in treating one patient? Such decisions are made covertly and in many cases unknowingly by those involved in service management. Some quality control in radiotherapy is vital if large scale errors are to be avoided. Yet huge sums may be spent on developing complex quality assurance schemes that may still not totally protect against major error.

Balancing the softer elements of the cancer patient's journey with the costs of providing the technology is a challenging task.

## The Big Picture

Cancer care is not just about treatment but also prevention and early detection. The main outcome indicators of the effectiveness of a cancer service have to be the incidence, morbidity and mortality from the disease. These can be improved by providing better care so that more will be cured or by detecting cancer earlier by screening, improving primary care and education or through prevention by lifestyle adjustment. The relative effort in each group will change in different communities as shown in Figure 2.

### Figure 2

### Outcome Differences Between
### Developing and Developed Countries

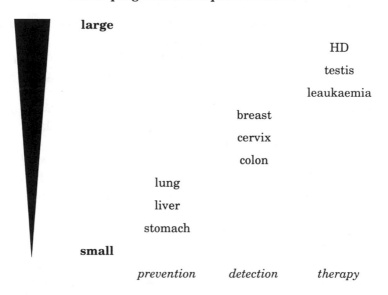

large

HD

testis

leaukaemia

breast

cervix

colon

lung

liver

stomach

small

prevention          detection          therapy

Note: HD (Hodgkin's Disease)

Treatment outcome differs enormously between developed and developing countries for Hodgkin's Disease, leukaemia and testicular cancer. For liver, lung and oesophageal cancer the results are the same when the patient is treated in Bangalore, Bognor or Boston. Once the disease spreads the patient dies. In the middle are breast, colorectal and cervical cancer where the effectiveness of current therapy depends critically on the stage of presentation. Screening, early detection and treatment quality all play a role in improving outcomes here. Dealing with the big picture involves moving resources around to achieve the best possible overall outcome.

## The WHO Cancer Priority Ladder

The WHO Cancer Programme aims to offer a comprehensive programme of expertise channelled through national health departments but with the full involvement of professionals already involved in cancer care. It is vital that this process encourages rather than stifles local enthusiasm and innovation

The central plank of this initiative will be the WHO cancer priority ladder.

*WHO Cancer Priority Ladder*

- tobacco control
- infection control
- curable cancer programme
- early detection programme
- effective pain control
- sample cancer registry
- healthy eating programme
- referral guidelines
- clinical care guidelines
- nurse education
- national cancer network
- clinical evaluation unit
- platform technology focus for region
- clinical research programme
- basic research programme
- international aid programme

This provides internationally agreed priorities for developing effective cancer control and will be carefully adapted to national circumstances. For example, tobacco control is an ubiquitous problem but the methods used to achieve long-term control will differ. Political consideration across a range of government departments will be necessary, especially in those countries where tobacco is a major source of employment and taxation. Infection control is an achievable target but is geographically very specific. Hepatitis B, for example, is fortunately rare in many developing countries and so universal vaccination strategies to reduce the incidence of hepatoma would be inappropriate.

Encouraging healthy eating and discouraging food manufacturing practices that increase fat and lower fibre content is a cheap intervention that will reduce the burden of cardiovascular disease as well as cancer. A curable cancer programme is essential as a tool for political persuasion. By looking at cancer positively people can be convinced to take action. Many in the past have been critical of the large sums spent on cancer patients by tertiary care facilities in many poorer countries. But the effective organisation of services into a hub-and-spoke model similar to that recommended in the UK's Calman Hine Report could focus care where it can be most effective.

Visiting review programmes, ensuring the availability of basic cancer surgery, radiotherapy and chemotherapy for potentially curable cancers, provide the first step in setting up a comprehensive cancer service. Agreed referral and clinical care guidelines which can subsequently be audited are an essential component. Furthermore this provides a cadre of interested professionals who can be encouraged to take a more holistic view of the cancer problem in their country. This may be enhanced by visiting review programmes such as the WHO Cancer Advisory Programme. This scheme, piloted in Morocco and Vietnam, provides site visits over three years by a group of experienced oncologists and epidemiologists. This allows leaders of the local oncology community to review in an informal setting their future plans as well as making personal international contacts. As well as reviewing cancer treatment capability such programmes encourage the local ownership of comprehensive cancer control from prevention through to palliative care by those involved in resource allocation.

Cancer registries can cost less than £7,000 ($10,000) per year to run and can provide an excellent database for time trends and measuring the impact of specific initiatives. These developments must also embrace the private sector. Increasingly the emergent middle class in poorer economies is turning to the private sector for health care. If specialist services are not available then there is no choice but to travel abroad, often at considerable expense, especially when compared to average earnings in many countries. Encouraging private sector involvement locally not only makes economic sense for future consumers but also provides for a technological trickle down effect.

Specialist nurse education is a further priority. A major problem is the considerable variation in level of education expected and achieved in many countries. Utilising all professional skills to their best advantage must take precedence over turf wars. The use of nurses in chemotherapy delivery areas and radiographers in the delivery of radiotherapy can be enhanced by introducing basic clinical decision-making skills following pre-set guidelines.

Psychosocial and information needs are best handled by those working closest to the patient and their family. Developing the role of the nurse must be a high priority in most settings. Evaluation, audit, education, scientific, clinical and epidemiological research are all interrelated. Good research can be done anywhere provided the problem addressed is carefully chosen. Unfortunately, there is a great tendency for physicians in developing countries to wish to emulate colleagues in the developed world. In doing so, unrealistic high technology projects are attempted which are doomed unless part of a pre-agreed international programme. Realistic assessment of research strategies with proper peer review is essential.

Platform technology programmes are the beginning of international aid. Once a successful national cancer programme is established many of its features can be adapted to neighbouring countries with similar characteristics. The WHO will continue to encourage this type of development alongside traditional methods of aid. Health care spending is an important but not exclusive factor involved in deciding the order or indeed the cut-off point.

The local epidemiology of cancer, availability of existing resources, education, culture and geography all need to be factored in.

Rationing in cancer care is a complex endeavour requiring a holistic view of the health care process. It seems essential that the relationship between doctor and patient is sacrosanct. It cannot be the point of direct rationing. Nor can it be buffeted by political expediency, sociological ideology or artificial accountancy. The rationing process must be carried out at a distance from an individual. Research and technological progress will continue to change medicine forever. But a doctor must always do what is best for his patient. In cancer care, like many high technology specialities, this will be a great challenge.

## The UK Scene: The Calman Report

The Expert Advisory Group on Cancer was set up by Sir Kenneth Calman in 1993. There were 15 members from a range of backgrounds. Its deliberations were lively, frank and informative. The bottom line was to recommend an oncological McDonalds. Success in the fast food industry requires rigid and unfailing quality control. The same lessons can be applied to cancer care. A series of around 30 cancer centres, mostly in teaching and research centres, would each link up to 10-12 cancer units, housed in surrounding general hospitals. Treatment guidelines, continuous audit and input of results from on-going research programmes, not just into surgery, radiotherapy and chemotherapy but also into the psychosocial aspects of cancer care, would stimulate a uniform high quality of practice. New drugs could be assessed for their effectiveness and decisions as to their financing made centrally. This would end the current postcode lottery where different purchasers have different attitudes to prescribing decisions. The report was uniformly welcomed by healthcare professionals, politicians, cancer lobby groups and provider units. It simply made good sense.

## Implementation

Despite these exciting potential developments, the implementation of the Calman report has so far been a saga of under-resourcing and bureaucratic muddle. There have been many agendas drawn up and many meetings. Forests have been felled to generate the paper consumed in reports, strategic analyses, focus groups, benchmarking exercises and background documentation. Some areas of Britain have been remarkably successful in getting a strategy together quickly and seemingly without fuss. In other areas conflict has arisen as purchasers with no experience in dealing with the problems of cancer care have adopted a confrontational stance with their providers, leading to acrimonious disputes, often spilling over into the media. Self-styled 'expert' teams, led by inappropriate managers, have consumed frontline staff's time during overly prolonged inspections in which the colour of the wallpaper figured as much as the availability of adjuvant chemotherapy. And clinicians are often incredibly resistant to change. There are clear indications of a volume effect in the treatment of certain cancers—groups that treat larger numbers of patients in a year have better survival results. But trying to prevent doctors from dabbling in a handful of cases each year is extremely difficult. This, of course, may be related to feared loss of lucrative private practice. But a major problem in all areas has been the lack of new resources to implement change.

## Money

The conflict has arisen mainly because no additional funding has been identified for what is a very ambitious programme. Hopes have been raised and not fulfilled at all levels, leading to demotivation, fragmentation and, on occasion, despair. What resources are realistically required?

We need a capital injection of about £100 million to set up the cancer units in general hospitals. Most are currently just 'peripheral clinics' open for one or two sessions a week in shared outpatient accommodation. If you ask at the hospital enquiry desk for the cancer unit or clinic you usually get a blank stare. It is vital that the unit has its separate identity in order to provide a focus for cancer care in the community it serves. Good connections with local GPs, community nurses and palliative care services are essential. Cancer information, educational programmes, psychosocial care and support groups can all be run from the cancer unit as well as conventional new patient and follow up clinics.

To create the right environment in most hospitals will cost between £100-500,000. Refurbishing or adapting an existing building will usually be the preferred option. The hospice movement and CT scanner appeals have demonstrated how effective local charitable fund-raising can be, provided that there is considerable professional enthusiasm for a project. Such fund-raising has been remarkably successful in many cancer centres, nearly all of which have made imaginative use of charitable and NHS funds to produce an excellent environment for patient care. Charities such as the Cancer Relief Macmillan Fund have made major strides in developing innovative projects around the country. Cancer information charities such as CancerBACUP will provide useful booklets about specific cancer types and also produce tailor-made brochures with local information. The current enthusiasm for complementary medicine has led to many volunteer organisations which will help in setting up simple complementary therapies within a local context. Co-ordinating these activities requires good day-to-day management and a strategic vision. But quite reasonably most charities, whether local or national, would like to see some NHS resource being used to develop the cancer units. This, at the moment, is the stumbling block. Very little investment has in fact been made.

### People

The real long-term investment for improving cancer services has to be in people. The number of specialist oncologists has to be increased dramatically. The Royal College of Radiology survey showed clearly that clinical oncologists here see far greater numbers of new patients than colleagues in comparable European countries. Some consultants are seeing over 1,000 new patients a year—20 a week. The UK average is 550 compared with 250 in France and Germany. To achieve this figure here would require a doubling of the consultant establishment. Although there has been a modest increase recently, no new sources of revenue have been specifically targeted for cancer. And, of course, any planned expansion must have a lag phase of at least five years to allow for an increase in the number of registrars in training, as the career structure is now vertical rather than pyramidal.

Cancer specialist nurses have proved to be one of the great success stories in improving the quality of care as perceived by patients. They are closely involved in chemotherapy delivery, the provision of patient information and in the organisation of palliative care. We need to develop their skills and numbers further. At least 600 more are needed so that there are at least two full-time equivalent posts for even the smallest of the countries' 300 cancer units.

The decline of organised religion and the loosening of family structures make a life-threatening illness such as cancer more difficult to handle for patients. Psychosocial care, through counselling, support groups and other interventions, is best provided by part-time staff working at unit level close to patients homes. A further 300 whole-time equivalent posts are required here. In addition, to run the unit smoothly requires an expansion in the number of receptionists, IT experts and health care assistants.

## Investment

There is good evidence that we are underfunding new developments in oncology compared with other countries. Recently, persistent bickering has taken place between purchasers and providers over the use of high-cost drugs. There is little evidence of wastage here. Data consistently shows that the NHS spends far more on treating constipation with laxatives than on chemotherapy for cancer. The Committee on Safety of Medicines assesses the potential effectiveness of a new drug and makes recommendation to the Medicines Control Agency. Once a product licence has been authorised the drug should be available on a uniform basis up and down the country. This is currently not the case, with varying forms of rationing in different areas.

Already NHS patients are being given the opportunity to pay if they wish to receive taxanes for metastatic ovarian or breast cancer. This puts an enormous strain on patients, carers and frontline healthcare staff and is not in keeping with the ethos of the service. Of course there are a variety of opinions as to the actual value of some of these drugs. Take Taxotere in a young woman with metastatic breast cancer. How much is six months of life really worth? Some purchasers hold the view that certain cancer centres treat far too aggressively when they should be offering palliation only. But life is a terminal illness for all of us and so all medical therapies are essentially palliative. We are therefore left with the question of assessing relative health gain. The difficulty comes from the divergence of opinions locally and the lack of an overall national policy. This situation will continue as long as priorities on cancer care are set locally.

There is no evidence so far that the current government is doing anything to halt the drift of the NHS into being a partial risk carrier. Thus expensive cancer chemotherapy may well join IVF, varicose vein and cosmetic surgery as essentially patient-financed options. If this is going to be the policy, then politicians should come clean now.

### Cancer Prevention

Optimal use of existing knowledge could reduce overall cancer incidence by one third. Tobacco control, dietary modification and prevention of infection with human papilloma virus could have a significant impact. Political action is needed to ban cigarette advertising and sponsorship which together result in young people taking up smoking. As we get more precise information about the relationship between diet and cancer, more specific messages will be possible. The green paper *Our Healthier Nation* (1998),[4] whilst admirable in some aspects, sadly glosses over specifics with regard to the public health aspects of cancer and certainly fails to consider any of the developments on the horizon.

The whole field of genetic risk assessment is a Pandora's box waiting to be opened. Identifying people with a high risk of getting cancer will allow tailoring of prevention and screening policies. Heath education, genetic assessment and counselling, even cancer vaccination, can all be part of a unit's work. If we can get the cancer network established, then future technology can be simply plugged into a well-oiled machine.

### The Bottom Line

The financial bottom line is shown in the table below. People are becoming aware of the high toll of doing nothing. The recent green and white papers specifically discuss cancer as a priority but do not point a clear way forward. *The New NHS*[5] makes much of the availability of hospital appointments to deal with symptoms that may be due to an underlying cancer. Unfortunately cancer presents in so many different ways that almost any symptom could be due to the disease, and there is simply no data to suggest that delay in diagnosis is a significant problem in the UK. Our primary/secondary care interface works well and few cancer patients ever wait for investigation and treatment. The current dialogue about improving services will just be hot air unless a significant investment is made in cancer service provision now. Besides the unquantifiable human misery, about 15,000 people die of cancer unnecessarily each year in Britain. We now have a robust plan acceptable to the politicians and the professionals. It is time for its full implementation so that national guidelines can be evolved and monitored. This will bring rationing where it belongs—into the open.

### Table 2
### *Costing Calman*

To provide 30 cancer centres and 300 cancer units

|  | Revenue £(million) | Capital £(million) |
|---|---|---|
| refurbishing areas to become identified cancer units |  | 100 |
| phased training into service |  |  |
| consultant staff |  |  |
| specialist nurses |  |  |
| psychosocial professionals |  |  |
| others |  |  |
| subtotal | 80 |  |
| increased cancer drugs budget | 10 |  |
| research into optimal care delivery | 10 |  |
| Total | **100** | **100** |

140

# *Notes*

**The Realities of Health Care Rationing in the NHS**
**John Spiers**
**Chapter 1: Rationing: The Challenge of PPE**

1 Heffer, S., *Like the Roman: The Life of Enoch Powell*, London: Weidenfeld & Nicolson, 1998, p. 535. On how government sets the context in which it seeks to control costs and demand, increase technical efficiency, set priorities and balance expectations and affordability see Smee, C.H., 'Bridging the gap between public expectations and public willingness to pay', *Health Economics*, Vol. 6, 1997, pp. 1-9. The empowered patient is not in the picture, which is instead concerned with 'improving the acceptability of the resource gap' (p. 7).

2 Heffer, *op. cit.*, p. 527.

3 Porter, M.E., *On Competition*, Boston MA: Harvard Business Review, 1998, p. 2.

4 Porter, *ibid.*, pp. 3-4. Smee, 'Bridging the gap', *op. cit.*, p. 7.

5 See also Spiers, J., 'If this is a question, is this an answer? Patients and empowerment: first principles, moral problems and patient benefit', in Ling, T. (ed.), *Reforming Healthcare by Consent: Involving Those Who Matter*, Oxford: Radcliffe Medical Press, 1999.

6 Mihill, C., *Hard Rations*, London: Association of the British Pharmaceutical Industry, 1999; *Daily Telegraph*, 21 January 1999, p. 11.

7 Thornton, J., *Should Health Screening Be Private?*, London: Institute of Economic Affairs, 1999, p. 28.

8 Brook, L., Hall, J. and Preston, I., 'Public spending and taxation' in Jowell, R. *et al*, (eds.), *British Social Attitudes, The 13th Report*, Aldershot: Dartmouth, 1996; Willman, J., *A Better State of Health*, London: Social Market Foundation/Profile Books, 1998. p. 17; Johnson, T., Larkin, G. and Saks, M. (eds.), *Health Professions and the State in Europe*, London, Routledge, 1995.

9 Wyndham, J., *The Kraken Wakes*, London: Michael Joseph, 1953, p. 216.

10 André, J., 'Learning to see: moral growth during medical training', *Journal of Medical Ethics*, Vol. 18, 1991, pp. 148-52; Spiers, J., *The Invisible Hospital and the Secret Garden, An Insider's Account of the NHS Reforms*, Oxford: Radcliffe Medical Press, 1995, esp. introduction; Enthoven, A., *Reflections on the Management of the National Health Service*, London: Nuffield Provincial Hospitals Trust, 1985, p. 9; Harrison, A., *Healthcare UK 1994/95: An Annual Review of Healthcare Policy*, London: King's Fund, 1995, p. 156.

11 Audit Commission reports: *Improving Your Image: How to Manage Radiology Services More Efficiently*, London: 1995; *By Accident or Design: Improving A&E Services in England and Wales*, London: 1996; *What the Doctor Ordered: A Study of GP Fundholders in England and Wales*, London: 1996; *Goods for Your Health: Improving Supplies Management in NHS Trusts*, London: 1996; *Efficiency Scrutiny Team, Prescription Fraud: An Efficiency Scrutiny*, London: NHS Executive, 1997. Also, Maynard, A., 'Loot is not the only route', *Health Service Journal*, 28 January 1999, p. 16; *The Fitzhugh Directory of NHS Trusts, Financial Information*, London: Health Care Information Services, 7th edition, 1999.

## Chapter 2: Re-defining Collectivism

1 Giddens, A., *The Third Way: The Renewal of Social Democracy*, Cambridge: Polity Press, 1998, p. 5.

2 *Ibid.*, p. 24.

3 I am indebted for this discussion to Porter, *On Competiton, op. cit.*, pp. 11-12.

4 Porter, *ibid.*, p. 12.

5 Private patient income figure from *Fitzhugh Directory, op. cit.*; Teisberg, E.O., Porter, M.E. and Brown, G.B., 'Making competition in health care work', in Porter, *op. cit.*, pp. 409-30.

6 *Daily Telegraph*, 3 November 1998, p. 11.

7 I am grateful to Dr. Anne Robinson for information on these points.

8 Berlin, I., *Four Essays on Liberty*, Oxford: Oxford University Press, 1992 edition.

9 Novak, M., *Is There a Third Way? Essays on the Changing Direction of Socialist Thought*, London: Institute of Economic Affairs,1998, p. 18. See Ham, C., 'Learning from the Tigers: Stakeholder Health Care', in Gladstone, D. (ed.), *How to Pay for Health Care: Public and Private Alternatives*, London: IEA, 1997, pp. 23-29.

10 Levinsky, N.G., 'Can we afford medical care for Alice C.? *Lancet*, 352, 1998, pp. 1849-51.

11 Quoted in David Hughes, review of *John Lehmann* by Adrian Wright, London: Duckworth, 1998, *The Spectator*, 28 November 1998, pp. 53-55.

12 Hayek, F.A., *The Intellectuals and Socialism*, Fairfax: Institute for Humane Studies, 1990, pp. 26-27 (first published 1949); also, discussion in Seldon, A., *The State is Rolling Back: Essays in Persuasion*, London: Economic and Literary Books/Institute of Economic Affairs, 1994; and in his *Capitalism*, Oxford: Blackwell, 1990.

13 Thackeray, W.M., *Vanity Fair: a Novel Without a Hero*, Harmondsworth, Penguin Books Edition, Stewart, J.I.M. (ed.), 1985, p. 663.

14 OECD Electronic Publications, Paris, *OECD Health Data, 1998: A Comparative Analysis of 29 Countries*; Office of Health Economics, *Compendium of Health Statistics*, 10th edition, London: OHE, 1997; *Health Service Journal*, 6 August; 1998, p. 29; Willman, *A Better State of Health, op. cit.*; *Daily Telegraph*, 5 February 1999, p. 11.

15 *The Times*, 4 December 1998, p. 7; *Sunday Telegraph*, 8 November 1998, p. 11. Oliver Morgan has in press a valuable study of European health care systems, which is forthcoming from the Social Market Foundation (and which I saw at the proof-stage of this essay). It offers a similar analysis on several issues, but with a different set of policy conclusions.

16 Private information, December 1998; Audit Commission, *Measuring Quality: The Patient's View of Day Surgery*, London, HMSO, 1991.

17 Willman, *A Better State of Health, op. cit.*, p. 3, p. 220.

18 McKeown, T., *The Role of Medicine: Dream, Mirage or Nemesis?*, Oxford: Blackwell, 1979; Evans, R.E.G., 'The dog in the night-time: medical practice variations and health policy', in Anderson, T.V. and Mooney, G. (eds.), *The Challenges of Medical Practice Variation*, Economic Issues in Health Care Series, London: Macmillan Press, 1990; McKinley, J.B. and McKinley, S.M., 'The questionable contribution of medical measures to the decline of mortality in the United States in the twentieth century', *Milbank Memorial Fund Quarterly, Health and Society*, Vol. 55, No. 3, 1977; Evans, R.G., Barer, M.L. and Marmot, R., *Why are Some People Healthy and Others Not?*, New York: Aldine de Gruyter, 1994.

19 Richardson, L., *Promoting Patient Participation in Portsmouth*, MBA Consultancy Project, Ashridge Management College, Herts, 1997.

20 See the seminal study, Green, D.G., *Working-Class Patients and the Medical Establishment*, London: Maurice Temple Smith, 1985; Dr. Green's *Reinventing Civil Society: The Rediscovery of Welfare Without Politics*, London: IEA, 1993, and 'Medical Care Without the State' in Seldon, A. (ed.), *Re-Privatising Welfare: After the Lost Century*, London: IEA, 1996; Gladstone, D. (ed.), *Before Beveridge, Welfare Before the Welfare State*, London: IEA, 1998. Also, Green, D.G., 'Public-Sector Monopoly or Competition? A Note for HealthCare 2000', [1995], privately circulated, p. 22.

21 Le Grand, J., 'Markets, Welfare and Equality' in Le Grand, J. and Estrin, S. (eds.), *Market Socialism*, Oxford: OUP, 1989. On hypothecated tax, see Duncan, A. and Hobson, D., *Saturn's Children, How The State Devours Liberty, Prosperity and Virtue*, London: Sinclair Stevenson, 1995; 2nd ed., London: Politico's Publishing, 1998, pp. 317-19; Mulgan, G. and Murray, R., *Reconnecting Taxation*, London: Demos, 1993.

## Chapter 3: The Three Principal Problems

1   Buchanan, J. and Tullock, G., *The Calculus of Consent*, Ann Arbor: University of Michigan Press, 1965; Buchanan, J., *The Limits of Liberty: Between Anarchy and Leviathan*, Chicago: University of Chicago Press, 1975; Tullock, G., *The Vote Motive*, London: Institute of Economic Affairs, 1976; Self, P., *Government by the Market? The Politics of Public Choice*, London: Macmillan, 1993.

2   Brash, D.T., 'New Zealand's Remarkable Reforms', Fifth IEA Annual Hayek Memorial Lecture, London: Institute of Economic Affairs, 1996; Douglas, Sir Roger, *Unfinished Business*, Auckland: Random House, 1993, p. 125.

3   Evident in the arbitrary nature of the 'double effect' approach of doctors to pain management in terminal conditions. See Michael Irwin, ' "Double effect" allows for "slow euthanasia" ', paper delivered to 12th international conference of the World Federation of Right to Die Societies, Zurich, 13 October 1998; and Spiers, J., *Who Owns Our Bodies? Making Moral Choices in Health Care*, Oxford: Radcliffe Medical Press, 1997.

4   Green, D.G., *Working-Class Patients and the Medical Establishment*, London: Maurice Temple Smith, 1985, and *Reinventing Civil Society: The Rediscovery of Welfare Without Politics*, London: IEA, 1993; Atkinson, D., *The Common Sense of Community*, London: Demos, 1994; Pelling, H., 'The working class and the origins of the welfare state', in *Popular Politics and Society in Late Victorian Britain*, London: Macmillan, 1968; Prochaska, F., *The Voluntary Impulse: Philanthropy in Modern Britain*, London: Faber and Faber, 1988; Prochaska, F., *Philanthropy and the Hospitals of London: The King's Fund, 1897-1900*, Oxford: Clarendon Press, 1992; Prochaska, F., *Royal Bounty*, London: Yale University Press, 1995.

5   Duncan and Hobson, *Saturn's Children, op. cit.*

6   Seldon, *Capitalism, op. cit.*

7   Mill, J.S., 'On liberty' (1859), with Introduction by Gray, J., (ed.), *On Liberty and Other Essays*, Oxford: Oxford University Press edition, 1991, p. 127.

8   Hume, D., *A Treatise of Human Nature (1739-40)*, Harmondsworth, Penguin Books, 1984, p. 532; Green, *Reinventing Civil Society, op. cit.*; and Duncan and Hobson, *Saturn's Children, op. cit.*, especially Chapters 13 and 14.

## Chapter 4: From a 1940s Mind-set to a Different World

1   Skidelsky, R., *The World After Communism: A Polemic for Our Times*, London: Macmillan, 1995; Barnett, C., *The Audit of War: The Illusion and Reality of Britain as a Great Nation*, London: Macmillan 1986, and

*The Lost Victory: British Dreams, British Realities, 1945-1950*, London: Macmillan, 1995.

See also Dearlove, J. and Saunders, P., *Introduction to British Politics: Analyzing a Capitalist Democracy*, Oxford: Polity Press, 2nd edition, 1991, p. 331, for an discussion of what a National Food Service would have been like.

It may be that the NHS itself, curiously, represents a sense of national defiance, something specific and British in a post-war world of international humiliations. Perhaps it can be explained as the rearguard act of *Pax Britannica*.

2    See discussion in Willman, *A Better State of Health, op. cit.*, pp. 192-94; Office for National Statistics, *Family Spending 1996-97*, London: The Stationery Office, 1997; *Daily Telegraph*, 28 January 1999, p. 15; *Social Trends*, London: Office of National Statistics, 1999.

3    Marinker, M. and Peckham, M. (eds.), *Clinical Futures*, London: BMJ Books, 1998, p. 7.

4    See Bell, J., 'The human genome', in Marinker and Peckham, (eds.), *ibid*; *Daily Telegraph*, 28 October 1998, p. 10.

5    Heffer, *Like the Roman: The Life of Enoch Powell, op. cit.*, p. 409.

6    Doctorow, E.L., *The Waterworks*, London: Macmillan, 1994, p. 85.

## Chapter 5: Deficits and Denials

1    Willman, *A Better State of Health, op. cit.*, p. 2; pp. 34-35; pp. 116-17. See also the long-running 'personal view' series in the *British Medical Journal*, reporting everyday experiences of how patients (who cannot go elsewhere) are dehumanised. Also, Thornton, *op. cit.*, on comparisons of public and private services in screening, residential care for the elderly, and dental care, and which are more efficient, innovative, responsive and which achieve improved quality. He argues that private medicine is not the problem; it is the solution.

2    Ivan Ellul, Deputy Head, Primary Care General Medical Branch, NHS Executive, to Institute of Health Services Managers conference, report in *Health Service Journal*, 2 October 1997, p. 16; Department of Health, *National Schedule of Reference Costs*, London: 1998; *Daily Telegraph*, 8 December 1998, p. 7.

3    Heffer, *Like the Roman: The Life of Enoch Powell, op. cit.*, p. 483.

4    André, J., 'Learning to see: moral growth during medical training', *Journal of Medical Ethics*, Vol. 18, 1991, pp. 148-52.

5    *Daily Telegraph*, 20 October 1998, p. 5; Sikora, K., 'Cancer', in Marinker and Peckham, *Clinical Futures, op. cit.*, pp. 74-95; Heffer, *Like the Roman: The Life of Enoch Powell, op. cit.*, p. 483.

6    Alan B. Shrank, Vice-President, Hospital Consultants and Specialists Association, *The Times*, 19 February 1998 (letters), p. 21; *The Guardian*, 1 October 1998, Consumer section, p. 14.

7    *Improving Quality in Cancer Care: The Current Role of Paclixatel in the First-Line Chemotherapy of Ovarian Cancer*, London: Royal College of Physicians, 1998; *Living with Ovarian Cancer*, London: Cancer BACUP, 1998; *Health Service Journal*, 5 November 1998, p. 7; *The Guardian*, 1 October 1998, *op. cit.* Much more information is analysed and published in the USA. See Sieverts, S.H., *No Pain - No Gain: Lessons from US Healthcare*, London: The Fabian Society, Fabian Briefing Number 5, 1996.

8    The All-Party Parliamentary Group on Breast Cancer, *Improving Outcomes in Breast Cancer*, London: House of Commons, 1998.

9    *Daily Telegraph*, 24 July 1998, p. 8; *Daily Mail*, 18 September 1998, p. 1, pp.4-5, 10; *Daily Telegraph*, 5 October 1998, p. 5; Warren, J. and Harris, M., *Come Back Miss Nightingale*, London: Social Affairs Unit, 1998; *Daily Telegraph*, 26 October 1998, p. 7; *The Times*, 29 June 1998, p. 21; *The Times*, 19 February 1998, p. 21; *The Times*, 17 August 1998, p. 21; *The Times*, 17 September 1998, p. 2; *The Guardian*, 23 December 1994; *The Times*, 25 June 1998; *Daily Telegraph*, 4 July 1998, p. 11; *Health Service Journal*, 17 September 1998, pp. 12-13; The All-Party Parliamentary Group, *Improving Outcomes in Breast Cancer*, *op. cit.*

10   *Daily Telegraph*, 24 July 1998, p. 8; Audit Commission, *The Doctors' Tale*, London: 1995.

11   *The Guardian*, 23 December 1994; *Stillbirths and Deaths in Infancy*, CESDI/Foundation for the Study of Infant Deaths, London: 1998; *Daily Telegraph*, 19 October 1998, p. 1.

12   *The Times*, 25 June 1998; *HealthCARE Today*, September 1998, p. 13; *The Report of the National Confidential Enquiry Into Perioperative Deaths*, London: NCEPOD,1996; Gallimore, S.C., Hoile, R.W., Ingram, G.S. and Sherry, K.M., *The Report of the National Confidential Enquiry Into Perioperative Deaths*, London: NCEPOD, 1997; Gray,A.J.G., Hoile, R.W., Ingram, G.S. and Sherry, K.M., *The Report of the National Confidential Enquiry Into Perioperative Deaths*, London: NCEPOD, 1998.

The late Mr. Brendan Devlin, originator (with Dr John Lunn) of the NCEPOD project, became 'less than popular with some colleagues', reported Kaye McIntosh, 'Enquiring mind', *Health Service Journal*, 14 January 1999, p. 13, on his death. Now credited with a lasting impact on surgical practice and ahead of his time, he was never knighted despite serving as head of audit and clinical effectiveness for the Academy of Royal Colleges, and in other senior posts including President of the British Association of Day Surgery. As Nelson de Mille noted, 'It is dangerous to be right when the state is wrong'. de Mille, N.,

*Spencerville*, New York: Warner Books, 1994.

13 *Daily Telegraph*, 2 February 1999, p. 11.

14 *National Schedule of Reference Costs, op. cit.; The Times* (Letters), 29 June 1998, p. 21; *Daily Telegraph*, 24 July 1998, p. 8; *The Times*, 17 August 1998, p. 2; *Daily Mail*, 18 September 1998, pp. 1-10; *Daily Telegraph*, 10 September 1998, p. 1; *The Times*, 11 September 1998, p. 15; *Daily Telegraph*, 3 October 1998, p. 8; *Daily Telegraph*, 26 October 1998, p. 7; *Daily Telegraph*, 3 November 1998, p. 11; *The Guardian*, 29 December 1998, p. 1.

15 On Bristol events, *The Times*, 19 February 1998, p. 11; *The Guardian*, 30 May 1998, p. 1 and *The Times*, 13 August 1998, p. 2; *Daily Telegraph*, 23 October 1998, p. 8. Also, *Response to the General Medical Council Determination on the Bristol Case*, Senate of Surgery of Great Britain and Ireland, London, October 1998; Klein, R., 'Regulating the medical profession: doctors and the public interest', in Harrison, A. (ed.), *Health Care UK 1997/98, The King's Fund Annual Review of Health Policy*, London: King's Fund, 1998. The public enquiry into the events at Bristol (expected to last two years and to examine 300 cases) opened on 27 October, 1998 and was then adjourned until spring 1999. See *Daily Telegraph*, 28 October 1998, p. 14. There is to be an independent enquiry into 'serious failures in clinical practice' of a gynaceologist at the South Kent Hospitals NHS Trust. *Daily Telegraph*, 6 February 1999, p.6.

16 *A First Class Service: Quality in the New NHS*, Leeds: Department of Health, 1998; Dr. William Pickering is preparing an important study on the requirement for external regulation by an independent body, and I am grateful to him for sharing with me his draft text. By contrast, see *Response to the General Medical Council on the Bristol Case*, London: Senate of Surgery of Great Britain and Ireland, 1998.

17 Sieverts, *No Pain - No Gain, op. cit.*

18 Ellul, *Health Service Journal, op. cit.*, p. 16.

19 Coulter, A. *et al.*, *Informing Patients: An Assessment of the Quality of Patient Information Materials*, London: The King's Fund, 1998; Mihill, C., *Hard Rations*, London: Association of the British Pharmaceutical Industry, 1999; *Daily Telegraph*, 21 January 1999, p. 11.

20 Medical Defence Union, London, *Problems in General Practice -Delay in Diagnosis*, issued privately to members but reported by *Health Service Journal*, 29 October 1998, p. 4; *Sunday Times*, 24 January 1999, Comment section, p. 18. Also, Dyke, G., 'Centre for best practice could straighten twisted economics', *The Times*, 16 February 1999, p. 36.

21 Goodkin, D.E., 'Interferon B therapy for multiple sclerosis', *Lancet*, Vol. 352, No. 9139, 7 November 1998, pp. 1486-87; European Study Group on Interferon B-lb in Secondary Progressive MS, *Lancet*, Vol. 352, No. 9139, 7 November 1998, pp. 1491-97; PRISMS (Prevention of Relapses and

Disability by Interferon B-la Subcutaneously in Multiple Sclerosis), *Lancet*, Vol. 352, No. 9139, 7 November 1998, pp.1498-1504; also, *Daily Telegraph*, 6 November 1998, p. 12.

22 For a recent case, see *The Independent*, 8 November 1998, p. 8, which reports that the £200,000 allocated to the drug in Nottingham funds only 18 of the 100 patients judged able to benefit from it. In the UK 1.5 per cent of MS patients get the drug, compared with 15 per cent in Australia; *Sunday Telegraph*, 17 January 1999, p. 17. I am grateful to Dr. R.J. Burwood for his comments.

23 *The Guardian*, 1 October 1998, Consumer section, p. 14; also, Sikora, in *Clinical Futures, op. cit.* The drugs are Taxol (breast cancer), and Taxotere (breast and ovarian cancer), which each cost £12,000 for a six-month course; Irnetecan (colon cancer - £8,000) and Gemcitabine (lung cancer - £6,000).

24 Winney, R.J., 'Choosing the best dialysis modality for the elderly patient', *European Renal Info*, 8, December 1998, p. 1; also, 'Economic factors weigh heavily in choice of treatment method', *ibid*; *Daily Telegraph*, 9 December 1998, p. 5; Department of Health, interim guidance on sildenafil (Viagra), HSC 1998/158; Consultation Letter from Secretary of State for Health, 21 January 1999; *Daily Telegraph*, 23 January 1999, p. 7. Vasomax, an alternative anti-impotence drug, may also be licensed by the Medicines Control Agency during 1999.

25 Willman, *A Better State of Health, op. cit.*, p. 19; Kingman, S., 'Renal Services in the UK are Underfunded, says Report', *British Medical Journal*, Vol. 312, No. 3, February 1996, p. 267.

26 *First Annual Report of the UK Renal Registry*, Bristol: The Renal Registry, October 1998; *Daily Telegraph*, 19 January 1999, p. 14.

27 Sieverts, *No Pain - No Gain, op. cit.*, p. 16.

28 Bosanquet, N. and Pollard, S., *Ready for Treatment*, London: Profile Books/Social Market Foundation, 1997, pp. 31-32.

29 *Daily Telegraph*, 9 December 1998, p. 5.

30 Willman, *A Better State of Health, op. cit.*, p. 16.

31 Health Service Commissioner's Annual Report for 1997/98, *2nd Report of the Select Committee on Public Administration, report of the Health Service Ombudsman for 1996-97*, London: The Stationery Office, 1998.

32 Judge, K., Mulligan, J-A., New, B., 'The NHS: New prescriptions needed?', in Jowell, R. *et al*, (eds.), *British Social Attitudes, The 14th Report*, Aldershot: Ashgate, 1997; Bosanquet, N. and Zarzecka, A., 'Attitudes to Health Services 1983 to 1993', in Harrison, A. (ed.), *Healthcare UK 1994/95, An Annual Review of Healthcare Policy*, London: King's Fund, 1995; Willman, *op. cit*, pp. 11-18.

33 *Consumer Concerns 1998, A Consumer View of Health Services*, National Consumer Council, London, 1998; *Daily Telegraph*, 1 August 1998, p. 23; Sainsbury Centre for Mental Health, *Acute Problems*, London, 1998; *Sunday Times*, 1 November 1998, news section, p. 15; *Daily Telegraph*, 10 November 1998, p. 12.

34 Sieverts, *No Pain - No Gain, op. cit.*, p. 15; Willman, *A Better State of Health, op. cit.*, pp. 22-24.

35 Help the Aged, London, *The Tip of the Iceberg*, 1997; Health Advisory Service 2000, London, *Not Because they are Old: An Independent Enquiry Into the Care of Older People on Acute Wards in General Hospitals*, 1998; NHS Executive, London, Health Service Circular 1998/220: *Standards of NHS Hospital Care for Older People*; 'The views of older people on hospital care', *The Health Summary*, Vol. xvi, No. 1, January 1998, pp. 11-17. Also, Audit Commission, *The Coming of Age: Improving Care Services for Older People*, London: HMSO, 1997; and Help the Aged, *Equal Access to Cardiac Rehabilitation*, London, 1998.

36 [Acheson Report], *Independent Enquiry Into Inequalities in Health Report*, London: The Stationery Office, November 1998. Also, The Office for National Statistics, *Health Inequalities*, London, 1998.

37 Melanie Phillips, 'An unhealthy interest in the wealth gap', *Sunday Times*, 29 November 1998, p. 19 (Comment section); *Daily Telegraph*, 27 November, 1998, p. 14.

38 See Pickering, W.G., 'Medical omniscience', *British Medical Journal*, Vol. 317, 19-26 December, 1998, pp. 1729-30; 'Does medical treatment mean patient benefit?', *Lancet*, Vol. 347, 1996, pp. 379-80; 'A nation of people called patients', *Journal of Medical Ethics*, Vol. 17, 1991, pp. 91-92; and 'Patient satisfaction: an imperfect measurement of quality medicine', *Journal of Medical Ethics*, Vol. 19, 1993, pp. 121-22.

39 Audit Commision, *By Accident or Design: Improving A&E Services in England and Wales*, London: 1996; Adam Darkins, 'Evidence-based medicine: a consensus dream or a practical reality', in Spiers, J. (ed.), *Dilemmas in Modern Health Care*, London: Profile Books/Social Market Foundation, 1997; Kind, P., 'Hospital deaths - the missing link: measuring outcomes in hospital activity data', Discussion Paper, 44, York: Centre for Health Economics, 1997; Saltman, R.B. and Rodrigues, J., 'Analyzing the evidence on European health care reforms,', *Health Affairs*, Vol. 17, No. 2, March/April 1998, pp. 85-108; Dyke, G., *The Times, op. cit.*, 16 February 1999. Baroness Jay has announced that participation in audit is to be compulsory for doctors. The General Medical Council is now (at last) proposing that all doctors will be required to prove they have kept themselves up to date; *Daily Telegraph*, 2 February 1999, p. 2. The process, however, is to remain one of self-regulation.

40 Audit Commission, *By Accident or Design, op. cit.*; Audit Commission, *United They Stand. Co-ordinating Care for Elderly People With Hip Fracture*, London: HMSO, 1995; *Daily Telegraph*, 31 December 1998, p. 11; *Daily Telegraph*, 27 January 1999, p. 1.

41 Willman, *A Better State of Health, op. cit.*, p. 29.

## Chapter 6: A Perspective on Deficits

1 Sieverts, *No Pain - No Gain, op. cit.*, p.15.

2 *Ibid.*, p. 15.

3 Perkin, H.J., *The Rise of Professional Society: England Since 1880*, London: Routledge, 1989, p. xiii.

4 Timmins, N., *The Five Giants, A Biography of the Welfare State*, London: Harper Collins, 1995; Klein, R., *The New Politics of the Welfare State*, London: Longman, 3rd edition, 1995.

5 Wyndham, *The Kraken Wakes, op. cit.*, p. 242.

6 See Spiers, J., '"Only a Novel!": Jane Austen, Hypertext, and the Story of Patient Power', in Marinker, M. (ed.), *Sense and Sensibility in Health Care*, London: BMJ Publishing, 1996; Porter, M., 'How information gives you competitive advantage', in *On Competition, op. cit.*, pp.75-98.

7 BMA leaders recently told the Secretary of State for Health that he must accept NHS rationing since a comprehensive NHS could no longer be afforded; *Daily Telegraph*, 9 October 1998, p. 6. The Health Care Financial Management Association warned that the NHS remains financially unstable; *Health Service Journal*, 15 October 1998, p. 7. NHS Confederation leader Stephen Thornton told the NHS 50th Anniversary conference that managers (!) must re-shape patient expectations, and set clear limits to care and treatment (!); *Health Management*, August 1998, p. 8. The exclamations are mine. See also Marsland, D., *Welfare or Welfare State? Contradictions and Dilemmas in Social Policy*, London: Macmillan Press, 1996.

8 Seldon, A., *The Dilemma of Democracy, the Political Economics of Over-Government*, London: Institute of Economic Affairs, 1998, p. 101.

9 Green, *Community Without Politics, op. cit.*, 1996. Also, Nozick, R., *Anarchy, State and Utopia*, Oxford: Blackwell, 1974, and Novak, M., *The Spirit of Democratic Capitalism*, London: IEA, 2nd edition, 1991.

## Chapter 7: Moving from 'Needs' to' Wants'

1 Letwin, S.R., *The Anatomy of Thatcherism*, London: Fontana, 1992, pp. 204-5; Willard, L.D., 'Needs and medicine', *Journal of Medical Philosophy* Vol. 7, No. 3, 1982, pp. 259-73.

2  Marsland, *op. cit.*, explores the needs/wants distinction. A third approach is the technical attempt to measure and compare capacity to benefit, using the scale of Quality Adjusted Life Years (QALY), or, for the disabled, Disability Adjusted Life Years. This approach seeks to assign a value to individual treatments which express the amount of benefit to a patient's quality of life or their freedom from disability related to the cost of that treatment. This can be seen as a further academic and bureaucratic attempt to substitute for market mechanisms and individual preference. See Maynard, A., 'Developing the health care market', *The Economic Journal*, Vol. 101, 1991, pp. 1277-86, and Maynard, A. and Bloor, K., *Our Certain Fate: Rationing in Health Care*, London: Office of Health Economics, 1999.

3  Harris, R., *No, Prime Minister! Ralph Harris Against the Consensus*, London: Institute of Economic Affairs, 1994; Harris, R. and Seldon, A., *Choice in Welfare*, London, Institute of Economics Affairs, series 1963-1987; Thornton, J., *Should Health Screening Be Private?*, London: Institute of Economic Affairs, 1999, pp. 15 and 16.

4  Caper, P., 'Database strategies for the management of clinical decision making', *New Perspectives in Health Care Economics*, London: Mediq Ltd., 1991, p. 65; and discussion of Department of Health, 'Health Service Indicators 1993-94', in Klein, R., Day, P. and Redmayne, S., *Managing Scarcity: Priority Setting and Rationing in the National Health Service*, Buckingham: Open University Press, 1996, p. 670.

5  *The Independent*, 2 January 1996, p. 1; *British National Formulary*, London: Pharmaceutical Press, 1998; *Health Service Journal*, 29 October 1998, p. 3.

6  Thornton, *Should Health Screening Be Private?, op. cit.*, pp. 16 and 15.

7  Proprietary Association of Great Britain, *Annual Report 1997*, PAGB, 1997, p. 20.

8  *Health Service Journal*, 2 October 1997, p. 16.

9  *Daily Telegraph*, 26 December 1998, p. 1.

10  *Daily Telegraph*, 25 March 1998, p. 5.

11  Jonscher, C., *Wiredlife: Who Are We in the Digital Age?*, London: Bantam Press, 1999, p. 198.

12  Keen, J., 'Should the NHS have a computing strategy?', in Harrison, A. (ed.), *Health Care UK 1997/98: The King's Fund Annual Review of Health Care Policy,* London: King's Fund, 1998, pp. 164-78.

13  Spiers, J., 'Only a Novel', in Marinker, *op. cit.* See also Negroponte, N., *Being Digital*, London: Hodder & Stoughton, 1995; and see the discussion in Spiers, *The Invisible Hospital and the Secret Garden*, introduction, *op. cit.*

## Chapter 8: Is Political Activism An Alternative To Financial Empowerment?

1   Beveridge, Lord, *Voluntary Action: A Report on Methods of Social Advance*, London: George Allen & Unwin, 1948, pp. 58-60; Green, *Reinventing Civil Society, op. cit.*

2   See www.doh.gov.uk/tables 98; *Daily Telegraph*, 10 December 1998, pp. 18-19.

3   Seldon, *Dilemma of Democracy, op. cit.*, p. 27.

4   O'Rourke, P.J., quoted in Duncan and Hobson, *Saturn's Children, op. cit.*, p. 82; Friedman, M., *Capitalism and Freedom*, Chicago: University of Chicago Press, 1962, p. 16; comment on voting, in Duncan and Hobson, op. cit., pp. 72-73; see also Ch.1.

5   Friedman, *op. cit.*, p. 16.

6   Duncan and Hobson, *Saturn's Children, op. cit.*

7   Green, D.G., 'The Morality of Welfare Reform: The Case for Unashamed Dismantling of the Welfare State', Address to Mont Pelerin Society Regional Meeting, Cape Town, South Africa, September 1995.

## Chapter 9: Self-responsibility and Competition

1   Porter, Introduction to *On Competition, op. cit.*, p. 1.

2   Nozick, *Anarchy, State and Utopia, op. cit.*

3   Green, *Re-inventing Civil Society, op. cit.*

4   Howarth, D., *1066, The Year of the Conquest*, London: Robin Clark edition, 1977, p. 14.

5   Green, 'The Morality of Welfare Reform', *op. cit.*

6   Beveridge, *Voluntary Action, op. cit.*, pp. 58-60.

## Chapter 10: Are We Living in Modern Times?

1   Doctorow, *The Waterworks, op. cit.*, p. 9.

2   Amongst a large output, see Giddens, A., *Capitalism and Modern Social Theory: An Analysis of the Writings of Marx, Durkheim and Max Weber*, Cambridge: Cambridge University Press, 1971; *Modernity and Self-Identity*, Cambridge: Polity Press, 1991; *Beyond Left and Right: The Future of Radical Politics*, Cambridge: Polity Press, 1994; *The Third Way: The Renewal of Social Democracy*, Cambridge: Polity Press, 1998; and 'The future of the welfare state', in Novak, M., *Is There a Third Way? Essays on the Changing Direction of Socialist Thought*, London: IEA, 1998, and Giddens, A. and Pierson, C., *Conversations with Anthony Giddens: Making Sense of Modernity*, Cambridge: Polity Press, 1998.

3   Vincent, J., 'Dressing up the new dawn', *The Spectator*, 23 January 1999, p. 29.

4   Giddens and Pierson, *Conversations with Anthony Giddens, op. cit.,* p. 57.

5   Giddens, *The Third Way, op. cit.,* p. 44.

6   *Ibid.*, p. 47.

7   *Ibid.*, pp. 30-31.

8   *Ibid.*, p. 59.

9   Giddens and Pierson, *Conversations with Anthony Giddens, op. cit.,* p. 94.

10  *Ibid.*, p. 231.

11  I owe these references to Carey, J., *Thackeray, Prodigal Genius*, London: Faber and Faber, 1977, pp. 136, 143, 160.

12  Giddens, *The Third Way, op. cit.,* pp. 63-64.

13  Giddens and Pierson, *Conversations with Anthony Giddens, op. cit.,* p. 101.

14  Giddens, *The Third Way, op. cit.* p. 37.

15  *Ibid.*, pp. 73-74.

16  *Ibid.*, p. 128.

17  Giddens and Pierson, *Conversations with Anthony Giddens, op. cit.* p. 135.

18  O'Brien, M., 'The sociology of Anthony Giddens: An introduction', in Giddens and Pierson, *op. cit.,* p. 11.

19  Berlin, *Four Essays on Liberty, op. cit.*, pp. 122-23.

20  Mill, *On Liberty, op. cit.*, p. 128.

21  Wyndham, J., *The Day of the Triffids*, London: Michael Joseph, 1951, p. 242.

22  Novak, *Is There a Third Way?, op. cit.*, p. 49.

23  *Ibid.*, p. 14.

24  Lloyd, J., 'Serf no more', in Novak, *ibid.*, p. 34.

25  Doctorow, *The Waterworks, op. cit.*, p. 152.

26  F.A. Hayek, *The Constitution of Liberty*, London: Routledge & Kegan Paul, 1960, p. 41.

27  Green, 'The Morality of Welfare Reform', *op. cit.* p. 39.

28 *Ibid.*, p. 36.

29 Feulner, Jnr., E.J., 'Foreword', in Hayek, F.A., *The Intellectuals and Socialism*, (1949) London: IEA, 1998, p. viii.

30 Blundell, J., 'Introduction, Hayek and the second-hand dealers in ideas', in Hayek, *ibid.*, p. 3.

31 Blundell, *ibid.*, p. 4.

32 Hayek, *ibid.*, p. 24.

33 Geoffrey Rivett, *Daily Mail*, 20 February 1998, p. 10; also, *From Cradle to Grave: Fifty Years of The NHS*, London: King's Fund, 1997; interview with Sir Michael Rawlins, reported in Barber, J., 'Weighing the evidence', *HealthCARE Today*, February 1999, pp. 14-15; *Health Service Journal*, 4 February 1999, p. 13.

## Who Is Responsible, Who Is to Blame?
## Bob Gilbertson

1 Macpherson, G., '1948: A turbulent gestation for the NHS', *British Medical Journal*, Vol. 316, No. 7124, 3 January 1998, p. 6.

2 *The New NHS: Modern, Dependable*, Cm. 3807, December 1997, London: The Stationery Office.

3 Rafferty, T., Wilson-Davies, K. and McGarock, H., 'How has fund holding in N. Ireland affected prescribing patterns', *British Medical Journal*, Vol. 315, No. 7101, 19 January 1997, p. 166.

4 *The Nature of General Practice*, Royal College of General Practitioners, Report 27.

5 Hibble, A., 'Practice nurse workload before and after the introduction of the 1990 contract for general practitioners', *British Journal of General Practice*, Vol. 45, January 1995, pp. 35-37.

6 Jacobson, L., Edwards, A., Granier, S. and Butler, C., 'Evidence-based medicine and general practice', *British Journal of General Practice*, Vol. 47, July 1997, pp. 449-52.

7 Ephram, S., 'Changing patterns of consultation in general practice: fourth national morbidity study 1991-1992', *British Journal of General Practice*, Vol. 45, June 1995, pp. 283-85.

8 Greenhalgh, T. and Gill, P., 'Pressure to prescribe', *British Medical Journal*, Vol. 315, No. 7121, 6 December 1997, p. 1482; Britten, N. and Ukoumunne, O., 'The influence of patient's hopes of receiving a prescription on doctor's perceptions and the decision to prescribe', *British Medical Journal*, Vol. 315, No. 7121, 8 November 1997, p. 1506; Macfarlane, J., Holmes, W., Macfarlane, R. and Britten, N., 'Influence of patient's expectations on antibiotic management of acute lower

respiratory tract illness in general practice', *British Medical Journal*, Vol. 315, No. 7117, 8 November 1997, p. 1211.

9   McBride, M. and Metcalfe, D., 'General practitioners' low morale: reasons and solutions', *British Journal of General Practice*, Vol. 45, 1995, pp. 227-29; Mathie, T., 'The primary care workforce: a time for decisive action', *British Journal of General Practice*, Vol. 47, January 1997, pp. 3-4.

10  Senge, P., Kleiner, K., Roberts, C., Ross, R. and Smith B., *The Fifth Discipline Fieldbook*, London: Nicholas Brealey Publishing, 1994.

11  Dixon, J. and Mays N., 'New Labour, New NHS', *British Medical Journal*, Vol. 315, No. 7123, 20-27 December 1997, p. 1639.

12  Whynes, D., Baines, D. and Tolley, K., 'Explaining variations in general practice prescribing costs per ASTRO PU (Age sex and temporary resident originated prescribing units)', *British Medical Journal*, Vol. 312, 24 February 1994, pp. 488-89.

13  The 'Red Book', NHS General Medical Services. Statement of Fees and Allowances payable to General Medical Practitioners in England and Wales.

14  Buckingham, K. and Freeman, P., 'Sociodemographic and morbidity indicators of need in relation to the use of community health services', *British Medical Journal*, Vol. 315, No. 7114, 18 October 1997, p. 994.

15  Senge, *et al*, *The Fifth Discipline Fieldbook, op. cit.*; Pinchot, G. and Pinchot, E., *The Intelligent Organisation*, San Francisco: Berrett-Koehler Publishers, c. 1994, 1996.

16  Berwick, D., Enthoven, A. and Bunker, J., 'Quality management in the NHS: the doctor's role', *British Medical Journal*, (1) Vol. 304, No. 6821, 25 January 1992, p. 235, (2) Vol. 304, No. 6822, 1 February 1992, p. 304.

17  Langley, G., Nolan, K., Nolan, T., Norman, C. and Provost, L., *The Improvement Guide*, San Francisco: Jossey-Bass Publishers, c. 1996; Davies, C., 'Quality improvements in general practice', *British Journal of General Practice*, Vol. 47, June 1997, p. 343.

18  Brown, J., Ridshill Smith, R., Cantor, T., Chesover, D. and Yearsley, R., 'General practitioners as providers of minor surgery: a success story', *British Journal of General Practice*, Vol. 47, April 1997, pp. 205-10.

## Rationing: An Inappropriate Response To A Real Problem
## Harry Burns

1   Doyal, L., 'Rationing within the NHS should be explicit. The case for', *British Medical Journal*, Vol. 314, 1997, pp. 1114-18.

2   Coast, J. 'Rationing within the NHS should be explicit. The case against', *British Medical Journal*, Vol. 314, 1997, pp. 1118-22.

3   Light, D., 'The real ethics of rationing', *British Medical Journal*, Vol. 315, 1997, pp. 112-15.

4   Eddy, D., 'Health system reform. Will controlling costs require rationing?', *Journal of the American Medical Association*, Vol. 272, 1995, pp. 324-28.

5   Light, 'The real ethics of rationing', *op. cit.*

6   New, W., 'The rationing agenda in the NHS', *British Medical Journal*, Vol. 312, 1996, pp. 1593-601.

7   Klein, R., 'Defining a package of healthcare services the NHS is responsible for: the case against', *British Medical Journal*, Vol. 314, 1997, pp. 506-09.

8   Mooney, G., and Lange, M., 'Ante-natal screening: what constitutes benefit?', *Social Science and Medicine*, Vol. 37, 1993, pp. 873-78.

9   *Ibid.*

10  Klein, 'Defining a package of healthcare services the NHS is responsible for: the case against', *op. cit.*

11  Hunter, D., 'Rationing healthcare: the political perspective', *British Medical Bulletin*, Vol. 51, 1995, pp. 876-84.

12  Hunter, D., 'Formulating a rational debate', *Health Service Journal*, Vol. 107, 1997, p. 18.

13  Swedish Parliamentary Choices Commission, *Priorities in Health Care: Ethics, Economy, Implementation*, Stockholm: Ministry of Health and Social Affairs, 1995.

14  Netherlands Scientific Council for Government Policy, *Public Health Care: Priorities and a Sound Financial Basis for Health Care in the 21st Century*, The Hague: 1997.

15  Hunter, 'Formulating a rational debate', *op. cit.*

16  Oregon Health Services Commission, *Prioritisation of Health Services: A Report to the Governor and Legislature*, Office of the Health Plan Administrator, 1997.

## Rationing Cancer Care
## Karol Sikora

1   Murray, C.J. and Lopez, A.D., *The Global Burden of Disease*, Boston, MA: Harvard University Press, 1996.

2   Sikora, K., 'Developing a global strategy for cancer', *European Journal of Cancer*, Vol. 35, 1999, pp. 24-31.

3   Chief Medical Officer's Expert Advisory Group on Cancer, Department of Health, *A Policy Framework for Commissioning Cancer Services*, London: Department of Health, 1995.

4   *Our Healthier Nation: A Contract for Health*, Cm.3854, London: The Stationery Office, February 1998.

5   *The New NHS: Modern, Dependable*, Cm. 3807, London: The Stationery Office,  December 1997.

# *IEA Health and Welfare Unit*

## *Advisory Council*

Professor Norman Barry (Chairman)
Professor Michael Beesley (London Business School)
Professor Peter Collison (University of Newcastle upon Tyne)
Professor Tim Congdon
Professor David Conway (Middlesex University)
Edgar Davies (Harvard University)
Professor David Gladstone (Bristol and Cornell Universities)
Thomas Griffin
Lord Harris of High Cross
Dr R.M. Hartwell
Professor Robert Pinker (London School of Economics)
Professor Duncan Reekie (University of Witwatersrand)
Professor Martin Ricketts (University of Buckingham)
Professor Peter Saunders (University of Sussex)
Professor John Spiers (University of Glamorgan)
Dr Jim Thornton (University of Leeds)

## *Staff*

Director: Dr David G. Green
Assistant Director: Robert Whelan
Editorial Assistant: Catherine Green
Admin Assistant: Nicholas Scrivens

## *Independence*

The Health and Welfare Unit is part of the Institute of Economic Affairs, a registered educational charity (No. 235351) founded in 1955. Like the IEA, the Health and Welfare Unit is financed from a variety of private sources to avoid over-reliance on any single or small group of donors.

All IEA publications are independently refereed and referees' comments are passed on anonymously to authors. The IEA gratefully acknowledges the contributions made to its educational work by the eminent scholars who act as referees.

All the Institute's publications seek to further its objective of promoting the advancement of learning, by research into economic and political science, by education of the public therein, and by the dissemination of ideas, research and the results of research in these subjects. The views expressed are those of the authors, not of the IEA, which has no corporate view.

# THE INSTITUTE OF ECONOMIC AFFAIRS

## Directors

| | |
|---|---|
| General Director: | John Blundell |
| Editorial Director: | Professor Colin Robinson |
| Health & Welfare Unit Director: | Dr David G. Green |

## Managing Trustees

Sir Peter Walters (Chairman)
Professor Michael Beesley
Robert Boyd
Michael Fisher
Malcolm McAlpine
Professor D. R. Myddelton
Sir Michael Richardson
Professor Martin Ricketts
Lord Vinson of Roddam Dene LVO (Vice-President)
Linda Whetstone
Professor Geoffrey Wood